THE CANADIAN
REGISTERED NURSE EXAMINATION
PREP GUIDE

FIFTH EDITION

A product of the Canadian Nurses Association  CNA

The clinical scenarios described in this book are entirely fictional.

No resemblance to real people or actual cases is intended.

Every effort was made to ensure the accuracy of the material presented in this book at the time of publication.

Given that policies, procedures and instructions can change at any time, candidates should always read and follow the directions provided by the regulatory authority and the presiding officer and the instructions contained in the Canadian Registered Nurse Examination.

Candidates use the information, materials and suggestions in this book at their own risk. Neither the Canadian Nurses Association (CNA) nor Assessment Strategies Inc., a subsidiary testing company of CNA, assumes any responsibility for candidates' performance on the Canadian Registered Nurse Examination.

ISBN 978-1-55119-283-3. 5th edition 2010
(ISBN 978-1-55119-938-2. 4th edition 2005)
(ISBN 1-55119-172-5. 3rd edition 2000)
(ISBN 1-55119-132-6. 2nd edition 1995)
(ISBN 0-88879-036-8. 1st edition 1992)

Printed in Canada

January 2010

■ TABLE OF CONTENTS

■ PREFACE

The Canadian Nurses Association (CNA) has developed the *Canadian Registered Nurse Examination Prep Guide* to help you prepare for the Canadian Registered Nurse Examination (CRNE). The prep guide contains the CRNE competencies and practice questions that are similar to those found on the CRNE. This prep guide is composed of multiple-choice questions and is specifically designed to familiarize you with the CRNE, introduced in June 2010.

The interactive CD-ROM that proved a success in the previous edition is back. With the CD-ROM, you have the added benefits of receiving immediate feedback, creating a performance profile and focusing your learning on specific competency categories with which you need practice.

The CRNE prep guide is part of a series of tools and resources offered by CNA under the banner *LeaRN®*. As a complement to the extensive study tips, questions and explanations in the prep guide, CNA also created the CRNE Readiness Test, available online. The readiness test is a shorter version of the CRNE and is designed to help you evaluate how prepared you are for the CRNE. CNA hopes that the prep guide and the readiness test will help you fine-tune your nursing knowledge and test-taking strategies.

As part of its commitment to the growth of the nursing profession, CNA continually reviews and updates the CRNE to ensure that entry-level registered nurses have the most complete and current knowledge to deliver safe, competent and ethical care in today's health-care environment.

CNA would like to thank the nursing regulatory authorities and the registered nurses who collaborated with us to produce this edition of the prep guide. We also want to wish you success in writing the CRNE and in your nursing career.

Canadian Nurses Association

■ ACKNOWLEDGEMENTS

The following people generously gave their time and expertise to the creation of *The Canadian Registered Nurse Examination Prep Guide* (5th ed.).

Doreen Campbell, Registered Nurses Professional Development Centre, Halifax, Nova Scotia

Heather Clarke, Carbonear General Hospital, Emergency Department, Carbonear, Newfoundland and Labrador

Leona Claxton, Kwantlen Polytechnic University, Vancouver, British Columbia

Eileen Coates, Misericordia Health Centre, Interim Care, Winnipeg, Manitoba

Kathie Conlin-Saindon, College of Nurses of Ontario, Practice and Policy, Toronto, Ontario

Donna Cooke, Saskatchewan Institute of Applied Science and Technology, Nursing Education Program of Saskatchewan (NEPS), Regina, Saskatchewan

Judith Cotton, University of Prince Edward Island, School of Nursing, Charlottetown, Prince Edward Island

Joyce D'Andrea, Lethbridge College, NESA Nursing Program, Lethbridge, Alberta

Mary Elliott, Humber College, School of Health Sciences, Toronto, Ontario

Laura Lee Evoy, Fort Smith Health and Social Services Authority, Acute Care, Fort Smith, Northwest Territories

Judith Hazel, Kwantlen Polytechnic University, School of Nursing, Surrey, British Columbia

Sonia Hill, Lake of the Woods District Hospital, Surgical Services, Kenora, Ontario

Cathryn Jackson, University of British Columbia, School of Nursing, Vancouver, British Columbia

Michelle Johnson, Assiniboine Regional Health Authority, Public Health, Boissevain, Manitoba

Kim Lake, Cape Breton University, Department of Nursing, Sydney, Nova Scotia

Liette-Andrée Landry, Université de Moncton, Campus de Shippagan, site de Bathurst, Bathurst, New Brunswick

Betty Ann Marriott, Aurora College, Health & Human Services, Yellowknife, Northwest Territories

Jan Mitton, Independent Practice in Capacity Assessments, Grimsby, Ontario

Jeanette Murray, Thompson Rivers University, School of Nursing, Kamloops, British Columbia

Patricia Patterson, Fanshawe College, Health Sciences Division, School of Nursing, London, Ontario

Gisèle Perrault, College Boréal, Campus au Nipissing, Mount Hope, Ontario

Diane Pew, Interior Health Authority, Summerland, British Columbia

Angela Rintoul, Nunavut Arctic College and Dalhousie University, Iqaluit, Nunavut

Marianne Schneider, Saskatoon Health Region, Saskatoon, Saskatchewan

Nathalie Senhouse, Regina General Hospital, Hemodialysis Department, Regina, Saskatchewan

Elizabeth Spracklin, Western Health, Organizational Development, Corner Brook, Newfoundland and Labrador

Marie St-Onge, Université Laurentienne, École des Sciences Infirmières, Sudbury, Ontario

Heather Taylor, Western Health, Health Promotion and Primary Health Care, Corner Brook, Newfoundland and Labrador

Brenda Tobin, Centre for Nursing Studies, St. John's, Newfoundland and Labrador

Kathy Watkins, Centre for Nursing Studies, St. John's, Newfoundland and Labrador

Ann Williams, Eastern Health, Mental Health and Addictions, Bay Bulls, Newfoundland and Labrador

Assessment Strategies Inc. Staff Contributors

A number of Assessment Strategies Inc. staff members contributed to the creation of this prep guide. Among them were people responsible for writing content and incorporating it into the prep guide and individuals responsible for planning and managing the activities related to the development of the prep guide.

Annik O'Brien, Project Consultant

Aida Hadziomerovic, Research Consultant

Rachel Buttle, Manager, Testing Services

Christine E. Logue, Project Administrator

CHAPTER 1:
USING THIS GUIDE

■ USING THIS GUIDE

INTRODUCTION

The Canadian Nurses Association (CNA) is pleased to provide the fifth edition of *The Canadian Registered Nurse Examination Prep Guide*. The purpose of the prep guide is to assist candidates who will be writing the Canadian Registered Nurse Examination (CRNE). This fifth edition of the prep guide is designed specifically for candidates who plan to write the CRNE on or after June 2010.

The prep guide is designed to familiarize you with the format of CRNE questions and to provide you with information on the content of the exam. The questions in the prep guide are based on the same set of competencies as the questions on the CRNE. For a list of all the competencies, see Appendix A.

In the prep guide, you will find a total of 200 multiple-choice practice questions. Approximately half of the questions are case-based questions and the other half are independent questions. Both case-based questions and independent questions are in a multiple-choice format; however, case-based questions are dependent on an introductory case or scenario, whereas independent questions are stand-alone questions. The questions represent common health situations of the population in those contexts or environments where entry-level registered nurses would work in a generalist role. As with the CRNE, the practice questions have been developed and reviewed by registered nurses who represent a variety of nursing programs, clinical backgrounds and regions of the country, and by test consultants who help ensure that the prep guide questions are similar to those that appear on the CRNE.

One of the most important features of the prep guide is that, for each practice question, rationales are provided for correct and incorrect answers. These rationales help explain nursing concepts and principles that are essential for entry-level practitioners. Although the questions in the prep guide are different from those on the CRNE, the general principles and concepts being tested are the same because the questions are developed from the same set of competencies.

Each question in the prep guide is also supported by two references. The majority of these references have been published within the past five years. The purpose of the references is to indicate that the correct answer within each question has authoritative support from at least two experts in the field and to provide you with a source for further reading and review. Every attempt has been made to use references that are up-to-date, accessible and accepted within the nursing community.

It is important to note that, although your score on the practice questions can give you some indication of how prepared you are for the CRNE, the prep guide is only one tool for promoting your success. The prep guide should be used to supplement and reinforce the knowledge and skills taught in your educational program.

Success on the CRNE depends on two main factors: (1) your knowledge of nursing principles and content specified in the CRNE competencies, and (2) your ability to apply this knowledge in the context of specific health-care scenarios based on those competencies. Make sure you are familiar with all the competencies listed in Appendix A because each question on the CRNE tests a specific competency.

CD-ROM

In order to enhance your learning experience, we have also reproduced the practice questions on a CD-ROM, enclosed in the inside back cover. The CD-ROM also contains 50 additional questions and rationales. The practice questions are blocked into two formats: case-based multiple-choice and independent multiple-choice. You can pick the format of the questions to be shown onscreen and the specific competency categories on which you wish to focus your learning. You can use the CD-ROM as a learning tool by seeing how you did after each question, or you can test yourself by answering all the questions and seeing how you did at the end. The CD-ROM will also generate a detailed performance profile that outlines in which areas you did well and on which areas you need to place greater emphasis. Using your performance profile you can then choose to redo questions related to one or more competency categories, thereby helping to focus your learning where you need it most.

The CD-ROM is designed to be very interactive and user-friendly. You can skip questions, pause at any point, save the partial data and move forward and backward through the questions. You can also transfer any written answers from the paper-and-pencil version of the prep guide onto the CD-ROM for easier calculation of the results and to display your performance profile. In addition, if you are connected to the Internet, there are links provided on the CD-ROM to the CNA website for an online CRNE prep guide satisfaction survey, an update on any changes to the CRNE prep guide and the CRNE Readiness Test site.

The CRNE Readiness Test

Once you have completed the prep guide practice questions, we encourage you to take the CRNE Readiness Test, which is available on CNA's website. The readiness test includes a whole new group of questions presented as a simulated online CRNE in a shortened format. Since the questions on the readiness test are different from those on the prep guide/CD-ROM, this test provides you with an additional opportunity to practise and strengthen your knowledge. Most importantly, the readiness test presents realistic conditions (e.g., the test is timed) for you to gauge how prepared you are to take the CRNE. The readiness test consists of former CRNE questions and is matched with the CRNE for level of difficulty. For more information on the readiness test, see chapter 8.

Chapter Summary

The prep guide consists of several chapters designed to help you with different aspects of your preparation. In this first chapter, you will learn the best way to use the prep guide and the enclosed CD-ROM, given your individual needs and the amount of time you have to prepare for the CRNE. Chapter 2 provides you with background information on the development, organization and format of the CRNE. It also explains the additional features available on the CD-ROM. Chapter 3 contains a variety of general exam preparation and test-taking strategies as well as specific strategies for answering multiple-choice questions. The practice questions are found in chapter 4 and on the CD-ROM. Chapter 5 explains how to use the answer key to score the practice questions and describes how the actual CRNE is scored. Chapter 6 shows you how to create your performance profile. Your performance profile is created automatically when you complete the practice questions on the CD-ROM. The rationales for each option in the practice questions are found in chapter 7 and are also available to you on the CD-ROM. Chapter 8 explains the CRNE Readiness Test, how to purchase the test and what your results will look like.

The bibliography lists all the references cited in the question rationales. Appendix A lists all the competencies that are tested on the CRNE and Appendix B contains a list of common abbreviations that appear on the CRNE. At the end of the prep guide, you will find a performance profile tally sheet to create your performance profile, blank answer sheets for the practice questions and a satisfaction survey. We encourage you to either mail or fax us the satisfaction survey with your feedback or submit it online through the link on the CD-ROM. Your opinion is important to us and will be considered when creating future versions of the prep guide.

METHODS OF USING THE PREP GUIDE

The questions in the prep guide are organized to mirror the CRNE in both number of questions and presentation. The prep guide, including the CD-ROM, can be used in different ways, depending on your particular needs and the amount of time you have before you write the CRNE. The three methods suggested below can be used independently or as part of a comprehensive study plan. Each method should be preceded by a review of chapters 1, 2 and 3 before advancing to chapter 4 (Completing the Practice Questions) or using the CD-ROM. Be sure to also review the competencies in Appendix A. The three methods differ in approach, according to the amount of time you have available before you write the CRNE. They cover periods of several months, one month and two weeks before the actual exam.

Method A: Several months before writing the exam

If you have several months before the exam, the prep guide is best used as a learning tool. Take the time to familiarize yourself with the prep guide and the format and layout of the exam. When you start answering the questions, answer one question at a time and immediately check whether you selected the correct answer. Then read the rationales for the correct answer and the incorrect options to gain insight into what made you answer correctly or incorrectly. On the CD-ROM, you will have an option to obtain immediate feedback after each response.

Method A gives you hands-on experience with exam questions and helps you identify any difficulties you may have with the exam format (e.g., not picking up on key words in the question, making unwarranted assumptions, reading too much into questions). On page 23, you will find a checklist of common test-taking errors, which will help you determine particular areas that you can improve on before writing the CRNE. Since this method does not simulate actual examination conditions, we recommend that you do not calculate your total score or make any inferences based on how you do at this time.

Method B: One month before writing the exam

Now that you are getting closer to the examination date, you will want to more closely simulate actual examination conditions while taking advantage of the time you have to address any areas in need of improvement. With this method, complete the practice questions, either entirely or in separate sections, before checking your answers against the answer key. Next, calculate your total score and interpret it according to the guidelines provided in chapter 5. Then develop your performance profile to identify your strengths and weaknesses.

The results of this self-evaluation should be used to identify gaps in your knowledge and skills. For example, if you know that you need improvement in a particular competency category, you can make your remaining study time more productive by concentrating on that specific area. Studying for the CRNE will also be made easier by consulting the reference books cited in the rationales for each question and listed in the bibliography. If you use the CD-ROM, you would not choose to obtain immediate feedback. However, you should still take your time to answer each question carefully and review the feedback and the rationales after you complete each section.

Method C: Two weeks before writing the exam

This method is based upon simulating the writing conditions of the CRNE as closely as possible. In this case, follow the instructions precisely, time yourself and use the answer sheets as if you were actually writing the CRNE. A good estimate of how long you would need to answer the CRNE is to give yourself approximately 1 to 1½ minutes per question, or four hours to complete all 200 questions. You may wish to simulate true examination conditions by arranging to take the practice questions with other students who are preparing for the CRNE.

Once you have completed all the questions, you can still benefit from creating your performance profile as suggested in method B, which will help you concentrate on specific areas where you may need improvement. When using method C, if you do not have time to obtain the references that correspond to areas where you need improvement, you may prefer to concentrate on the rationales provided for each practice question.

Treat completing the practice questions on the CD-ROM as you would if you were completing the questions with paper and pencil, following all the administrative guidelines (time limits, no reference materials, etc.). Applying method C on the CD-ROM means that you would not obtain immediate feedback. When you have completed all the practice questions, your result and a performance profile will be generated automatically and you will be able to see how well you did overall.

After completing the questions in the prep guide, you will have a better idea about how well prepared you are to take the CRNE. As a final step, it may be beneficial to take the online CRNE Readiness Test. The readiness test can serve as the final check to ensure that you have done everything you can to prepare for the CRNE.

Good luck!

CHAPTER 2:
BACKGROUND ON THE CRNE

■ BACKGROUND ON THE CRNE

Each Canadian provincial and territorial regulatory authority for nurses is responsible for ensuring that all entry-level registered nurses within its jurisdiction meet an acceptable level of competence before they are licensed to practise as registered nurses. This level of competence is measured partly by the CRNE, which is developed and owned by CNA and administered by all provincial and territorial regulatory authorities,[1] except in Quebec. This process ensures a common standard that all registered nurses practising in these jurisdictions must meet.

CNA, through Assessment Strategies Inc., has been developing the CRNE since 1970. Before that, jurisdictions made their own arrangements for testing and most used exams developed in the United States. Originally, each test booklet represented a separate clinical area (e.g., medicine, surgery, pediatrics). Since August 1980, however, the exam content has been integrated such that the material from areas such as pharmacology, nutrition and growth and development is incorporated into a variety of health-care situations that a registered nurse entering practice as a generalist is most likely to encounter.

The CRNE is developed to measure an explicitly defined content domain that consists of the competencies expected of registered nurses beginning to practise. In the case of the CRNE, the content domain of interest consists of the competencies an entry-level registered nurse must have to practise safely, ethically and effectively. In 2008, a thorough review and updating of these competencies resulted in the creation of a new set of competencies that form the basis of the June 2010 and later versions of the exam (see Appendix A). These new competencies, and the guidelines and specifications that outline the way they are measured on the CRNE, are presented in the CNA publication *Blueprint for the Canadian Registered Nurse Examination June 2010 - May 2015*. For June 2010 - May 2015, the CRNE consists of 180-200 operational questions.

As with the previous exams, the new version of the CRNE is the end result of many test development activities that take place throughout a two-year period. Nurse educators, clinicians and administrators from across Canada create and evaluate exam questions with assistance from Assessment Strategies Inc.

CRNE DEVELOPMENT GUIDELINES

This section presents the guidelines for structural and contextual variables that guide the development of the CRNE.

STRUCTURAL VARIABLES

Structural variables are those characteristics that determine the general design and appearance of the exam. They include the length of the exam, the format and presentation of the exam questions, test equating, the competency categories and the taxonomy levels of cognitive ability.

Exam Length

The exam consists of between 180 and 200 operational questions. This number does not include the experimental questions that appear on the CRNE.

With 148 competencies to measure and a sound sampling approach for these competencies, an exam of between 180 and 200 questions is sufficient to make both reliable and valid decisions about a candidate's readiness to practise nursing safely, ethically and effectively.

[1] The regulatory authorities impose eligibility criteria, such as the completion of an approved program of nursing education, which provide the added information required to decide on an individual's readiness to practise nursing.

Question Presentation and Format

The exam consists of multiple-choice questions only, presented either as case-based or as independent questions. For case-based questions, a set of approximately three to five questions is associated with a brief health-care scenario. Independent questions contain all the information necessary to answer the question.

Test Equating

Test equating is done to ensure that candidates are required to achieve the same standard for licensure regardless of the exam they write. Test equating can be accomplished by means of a statistical procedure that adjusts for the difficulty of questions on the various forms of the exam so that a consistent standard for licensure is maintained (e.g., by using item response theory).

COMPETENCY FRAMEWORK

A framework was developed to identify and organize the competencies that the CRNE should assess. The framework reflects a primary health-care nursing model. The framework and definitions of the four framework categories are presented below. The number of competencies in each category is indicated in parentheses following the category name. Because some of the competencies lend themselves to being placed in one or more categories, these four categories should be viewed simply as an organizing framework.

Professional Practice (28 competencies)

Registered nursing competencies in this category focus on personal professional growth, as well as intraprofessional, interprofessional and intersectoral practice responsibilities. Each registered nurse is accountable for safe, compassionate, competent and ethical nursing practice. Professional practice occurs within the context of the *Code of Ethics for Registered Nurses* (CNA, 2008), provincial/territorial standards of practice and scope of practice, legislation and common law. Registered nurses are expected to demonstrate professional conduct as reflected by the attitudes, beliefs and values espoused in the *Code of Ethics for Registered Nurses.*

Professional registered nurse practice is self-regulating. Nursing practice requires professional judgment, interprofessional collaboration, leadership, management skills, cultural safety, advocacy, political awareness and social responsibility. Professional practice includes awareness of the need for, and the ability to, ensure continued professional development. This ability involves the capacity to perform self-assessments, seek feedback and plan self-directed learning activities that ensure professional growth. Registered nurses are expected to use knowledge and research to build an evidence-informed practice.

Nurse-Client Partnership (14 competencies)

Registered nursing competencies in this category focus on therapeutic use of self, communication skills, nursing knowledge and collaboration to achieve the client's identified health goals. The nurse-client partnership is a purposeful, goal-directed relationship between nurse and client that is directed at advancing the best interest and health outcome of clients. The therapeutic partnership is central to all nursing practice and is grounded in an interpersonal process that occurs between the nurse and client (Registered Nurses' Association of Ontario, 2002). The registered nurse approaches this partnership with self-awareness, trust, respect, openness, empathy and sensitivity to diversity, reflecting the uniqueness of the client.

Health and Wellness (27 competencies)

Registered nursing competencies in this category focus on recognizing and valuing health and wellness. The category encompasses the concept of population health and the principles of primary health care. Registered nurses partner with clients to develop personal skills, create supportive environments for health, strengthen community action, reorient health services and build healthy public policy. Nursing practice is influenced by continuing competency, determinants of health, life phases, demographics, health trends, economic and political factors, evidence-informed knowledge and research.

Changes in Health (79 competencies)

Registered nurse competencies in this category focus on care across the lifespan of the client who is experiencing changes in health. The competencies in this category thus focus on health promotion and illness prevention activities, as well as on acute, chronic, rehabilitative, palliative and end-of-life care. Such nursing actions may be delivered across a range of settings. Essential aspects of nursing care include critical inquiry, safety, solution-focused approaches, reflective practice and evidence-informed decision-making. Registered nurses collaborate with clients and other health-care professionals to identify health priorities and empower clients to improve their own health. In responding to and managing health situations, registered nurses promote optimal quality of life and development of self-care capacity and dignity during illness and during the dying and death process.

TAXONOMY LEVELS OF COGNITIVE ABILITY

To ensure that competencies are measured at different levels of cognitive ability, each question on the CRNE is classified into one of three levels: (1) knowledge/comprehension, (2) application, and (3) critical thinking. These levels are adapted from the taxonomy of cognitive abilities originally developed by Bloom (1956).

Knowledge/Comprehension

This level combines the ability to recall previously learned material with the ability to understand its meaning. It includes such mental abilities as knowing and understanding definitions, facts and principles, and interpreting data (e.g., identifying the effects of certain drugs). Knowledge/comprehension questions make up a minimum of 10% of the CRNE.

Application

This level refers to the ability to apply knowledge and learning to new or practical situations. It includes applying rules, methods, principles and nursing theories in providing care (e.g., applying principles of drug administration and concepts of comfort and safety). Application questions make up a minimum of 40% of the CRNE.

Critical Thinking

The third level of the taxonomy deals with higher level thinking processes. It includes the abilities to judge the relevance of data, to deal with abstractions and to solve nursing problems (e.g., differentiating priorities of care, evaluating the effectiveness of nursing actions). The registered nurse should be able to identify cause-and-effect relationships, distinguish between relevant and irrelevant data, formulate valid conclusions and make judgments concerning the needs of clients.[2] Critical thinking questions make up a minimum of 40% of the CRNE.

---

[2] The term "client" refers to an individual, family, group, population or community.

CONTEXTUAL VARIABLES

Contextual variables qualify the content domain by specifying the nursing contexts in which the CRNE questions are set. They include client, lifespan, diversity, health situation and practice environment.

Client

The exam includes questions related to the following:

- individuals;

- families; and

- groups, populations and communities.

Lifespan

The exam includes questions related to the lifespan, from preconception through to advanced age, including end of life. Exam questions reflect health situations relevant to all life phases:

- the period between preconception and birth;

- newborn and infant (birth to 12 months);

- young child (1-6 years);

- older child (7-12 years);

- adolescent (13-18 years);

- young adult (19-35 years);

- middle adult (36-64 years);

- older adult (65-79 years); and

- adult of advanced age (80+ years).

The distribution of the exam questions may be guided by the demographics of clients (e.g., projections of Canadian population statistics by age and gender). Ongoing reference to current trends (e.g., health services utilization statistics, CNA public policy and nursing policy documents) and the competencies inform exam question development and revision.

Diversity

Exam questions reflect the diversity inherent in client populations, without introducing stereotypes. The exam does not test candidates' knowledge of specific values, beliefs and practices linked to individuals.

Health Situation

Because the client is viewed holistically, the client's biophysical, psychosocial and spiritual dimensions form the basis for every health situation. The particular health situations presented on the exam are based on the assumptions on which the competencies are founded (see Appendix A). On the basis of the specified contextual variables and the elements mentioned above, exam questions that test a cross-section of health situations are developed.

Practice Environment

One of the assumptions underlying the competencies is that the practice environment of the entry-level registered nurse can be any setting or circumstance within which nursing is practised. It includes the sites of activity (e.g., institutions, clinics, homes, schools, agencies), programs designed to address a client's health, and resources available to the client and the registered nurse. Furthermore, many competencies are applicable to a variety of settings. The practice environment is specified only where required to provide guidance to the candidate.

Summary Chart: CRNE DEVELOPMENT GUIDELINES

STRUCTURAL VARIABLES

Exam Length	180-200 operational questions*
Question Format and Presentation	Format: Multiple-choice questions Presentation: Questions are presented as case-based and independent questions.
Test Equating	Anchor questions are used to accomplish test equating.
Competency Categories	Professional Practice 14-24% of questions Nurse-Client Partnership 9-19% of questions Health and Wellness 21-31% of questions Changes in Health 40-50% of questions
Taxonomy of Cognitive Ability	Knowledge/Comprehension Minimum of 10% of questions Application Minimum of 40% of questions Critical Thinking Minimum of 40% of questions

CONTEXTUAL VARIABLES

Client	Questions pertain to individuals, families, groups, populations and communities.
Lifespan	Questions reflect health situations relevant to all life phases.
Diversity	Questions reflect the diversity inherent in client populations, without introducing stereotypes.
Health Situation	Health situations reflect the continuum of health and illness.
Practice Environment	The practice environment can be any setting or circumstance within which the entry-level registered nurse practises. Most of the competencies are not setting-dependent; however, the practice environment is specified where necessary.

*This number does not include the experimental questions that appear on the CRNE.

HOW THE CRNE IS ORGANIZED

The CRNE is administered as a single test form consisting of 180 to 200 multiple-choice case-based and independent questions. Each question is designed to measure a specific competency. Candidates are given four hours to complete the exam.

Multiple-Choice Questions

Each multiple-choice question is composed of two distinct elements: (1) the stem, and (2) the options. The stem is the introductory part of the question that presents the examinee with a question or problem. The options are the alternatives (e.g., words, statements, numbers) from which the examinee is to select the correct or best answer to the question or problem posed in the stem. Each question has four options: the correct response, representing the correct (or best) answer, and three distracters that are plausible but incorrect (or less adequate) options intended to distract the examinee who is uncertain of the correct response.

Multiple-choice questions may be presented within a case (i.e., a brief introductory case text accompanied by three to five related questions) or independently (i.e., stand-alone questions that are not specifically connected with any other text or questions). Questions associated with a case represent a plausible sequence of events.

The following pages show examples of the types of questions used on the CRNE.

CASE QUESTION

Mr. Heitkemper, 63 years old, is admitted with unstable angina. He has a history of type 2 diabetes and hypertension.

QUESTIONS 1 to 5 refer to this case.

1. The nurse finds Mr. Heitkemper in moderate distress. He is pale with cool, clammy skin with his fist clenched over his chest. What is the priority nursing action?

    1. Ask Mr. Heitkemper to rate his pain on a scale of 1 to 10.

    2. Administer oxygen at 2 L via nasal cannula.

    3. Take his vital signs and auscultate heart sounds.

    4. Administer a nitrate followed by a narcotic analgesic if needed.

2. Mr. Heitkemper states that he is experiencing chest pain. Which description of chest pain would most likely be related to angina?

    1. It radiates to the neck and back.

    2. It is a stabbing, sharp sub-sternal pain.

    3. It is relieved by sitting upright.

    4. It worsens when taking deep breaths.

3. Mr. Heitkemper is scheduled for a coronary angioplasty and stent placement. When preparing Mr. Heitkemper, what should the nurse explain to the client?

    1. He will have a small incision on his chest.

    2. He may need to lie flat with his leg immobilized.

    3. He will need to do deep breathing and coughing exercises.

    4. Information will be provided about myocardial infarction.

4. The nurse provides teaching to Mr. Heitkemper regarding recommended lifestyle changes. Which response by Mr. Heitkemper would show that he has understood the instruction?

    1. He will stop adding salt and sugar to his food until he is feeling better.

    2. His wife does the shopping and cooking and she is the one who needs the information.

    3. He will drink only one glass of milk a day and add just a little salt when preparing foods.

    4. It will be difficult to follow the diet changes and he is not sure he can do it without help.

5. Following discharge, Mr. Heitkemper continues to take digoxin (Lanoxin) and nifedipine (Adalat). What adverse effects of this combination of drugs must he recognize and report to his physician?

    1. Increased urination and swollen ankles

    2. Changes in vision and loss of appetite

    3. Changes in skin colour or weight gain

    4. Bruising and bleeding gums

END OF SAMPLE CASE

INDEPENDENT QUESTIONS

1. Which nursing measure would facilitate a client's body image acceptance following a total laryngectomy and tracheostomy?

    1. Demonstrate a sympathetic approach when providing the client's tracheostomy care.

    2. Emphasize what the client can do within the limitations resulting from the treatment.

    3. Encourage the client's family to refrain from discussing the tracheostomy while visiting.

    4. Reassure the client that following discharge, there can be a complete return to pre-hospitalization activities.

2. What should the nurse do when a physician's order for an analgesic seems excessive?

    1. Assess the client closely for side effects after giving the medication.

    2. Seek clarification from the physician before giving the medication.

    3. Give the medication and document the concern in the nursing notes.

    4. Withhold the medication and document the reason in the nursing notes.

END OF INDEPENDENT QUESTIONS

CHAPTER 3:
EXAM PREPARATION AND TEST-TAKING STRATEGIES

■ EXAMINATION PREPARATION AND TEST-TAKING STRATEGIES

This chapter will help you prepare to write the CRNE by reviewing what you need to do before and during the exam, what you need to bring to the examination centre and how you can best perform on multiple-choice questions.

BEFORE THE CRNE

Arrange to Write the CRNE

In order to write the CRNE, you must contact the regulatory authority in the province or territory in which you wish to write the exam. Their staff will inform you of the documentation you must provide to register for the exam, the process by which you will be assessed for eligibility to take the exam, as well as the fee you will have to pay. A list of regulatory authorities that use the CRNE can be found on the CNA website.

The Canadian Nurses Association and Assessment Strategies Inc., in conjunction with the regulatory authorities, will authorize reasonable and appropriate modifications to the CRNE administration procedures in order to accommodate candidates with special needs. For further information, contact the regulatory authority in your jurisdiction.

Read *The Canadian Registered Nurse Examination Prep Guide*

The prep guide, including the CD-ROM, contains information that will help you prepare for the CRNE. The questions, feedback and references available provide direction on essential nursing content. The list of competencies found in Appendix A will also help you focus on the area of study.

Take the Practice Questions in the Prep Guide

Taking the practice questions under conditions that are as close as possible to those of the actual exam is a great way to prepare and to ensure that there will be no surprises. Give yourself the right amount of time (approximately four hours) to complete the 200 questions in the prep guide and do not look ahead to the answers. To simulate true examination conditions, arrange to take the practice questions with other students who are also preparing for the exam. For more information on using the prep guide, refer to Methods of Using the Prep Guide in chapter 1.

Use the Information from Your Performance Profile

By conducting an analysis of your performance on the practice questions, you will be able to identify your strengths and weaknesses. Use this information to focus your studying on areas of weakness. If you are taking the paper-and-pencil version of the practice questions, use the information on how to create your performance profile found in chapter 6. With the CD-ROM version, your performance profile is generated automatically. If you take the paper-and-pencil version of the practice questions, you can manually transfer your results from the answer sheet to the CD-ROM. The computer will then calculate your results automatically and produce a performance profile.

Study Effectively

Select a place that is quiet and free from distractions yet comfortable for studying. Develop a study plan, dividing your time between specific topics or sections. Pace yourself, keeping in mind that five 2-hour sessions are likely to be more beneficial than two 5-hour periods. Monitor your progress and revise your schedule as necessary.

Test Yourself with the CRNE Readiness Test

The CRNE Readiness Test is an online simulation of the CRNE, in a shortened format. It will assist you in assessing your readiness for the CRNE by providing you feedback on your performance in relation to recent passing standards for the CRNE and where you need to focus your study efforts. The readiness test consists of former CRNE questions and is matched with the CRNE for level of difficulty. You can find more information about the CRNE Readiness Test on the CNA website.

Prepare for the Examination Day

Check the location of the examination centre and examination room and determine how much time you will need to get there. If necessary, do a practice run and confirm bus schedules or the availability of parking. It is important to be alert and focused when you write the exam. Be sure to get plenty of rest and to eat a suitable meal before you arrive at the examination centre.

What to Bring to the CRNE

Identification

You must bring your candidate identification card, issued by your regulatory authority, and a valid government-issued photo identification document, such as a passport, a driver's licence or a health card. The regulatory body will also inform you as to whether you are required to present additional identification.

Pencils and Eraser

Unless otherwise advised, bring two or three medium-soft (HB) pencils and a soft pencil eraser.

What NOT to Bring

Books, paper, notes, calculators and other aids are not permitted in the examination room. All electronic devices, including organizers and communication devices such as pagers and cellular telephones, are also prohibited. You may consider leaving these items at home as the regulatory authorities, CNA and Assessment Strategies Inc., are not responsible for the security of any personal items brought to the examination writing centres.

What to Wear

Remember that you will be sitting for hours. Wear comfortable and layered clothing that you can put on or remove if the temperature is too cold or too warm.

DURING THE CRNE

Listen to All Announcements

The presiding officer will inform you of important details, such as how long you have to complete the exam and how and where to hand in your test booklet and answer sheet.

Read the Test Booklet Instructions

It is essential that you have a clear understanding of what you are expected to do. If you do not understand what you have been told or what you have read, ask questions before the exam officially begins.

Complete All Information Accurately

You will be required to fill in certain information on your answer sheet and test booklet (e.g., your candidate number from your candidate identification card). Errors made in completing this information can delay the scoring of your exam. Be sure that for each question, you have recorded a single answer in the appropriate place on the answer sheet.

Answering Multiple-Choice Questions

Consider each question separately. Try not to rush, but do not spend more than 1 to 1½ minutes on any individual question. If you do not know the answer to a question, skip it and return to it later. If you still do not know the answer, make a guess.

If you do not answer all the questions in sequence, make sure that the oval you are filling in on your answer sheet is aligned with the correct question number.

When you decide on a correct answer, mark your choice on the answer sheet before moving on to the next question. Do not circle all the answers in the test booklet and transfer them to the answer sheet at the end because you could run out of time. All answers must be recorded on your answer sheet. Credit is not given for answers in your test booklet.

Changing Your Answer

If you decide to change an answer, make sure that the original answer is erased completely. If it appears as though you have two options selected for the same question, the scanner will score it as a wrong answer. Similarly, avoid making stray marks on your answer sheet that the computer could inadvertently pick up as answers to questions.

Be cautious about changing your answer. Very often your first choice is correct. Making a new selection is only advantageous if you are confident that the new option is correct.

Read the Question Carefully

Concentrate on what is being asked in the question and relate it to the data provided. Do not make any assumptions unless they are directly implied.

Pick out *important* words that relate to the question. For example, in some questions you may be asked for the most appropriate *initial* response by the nurse, but you should be aware that questions that follow may ask for the nurse's most *ethical* response or the nurse's most *therapeutic* response. Reviewing the practice questions will help you recognize key words that will appear on the CRNE.

Guessing

If you do not know the correct answer you can make a guess. There is no penalty for guessing. You will receive 0 points for an incorrect answer and 1 point for a correct answer.

STRATEGIES FOR MULTIPLE-CHOICE QUESTIONS

A thorough understanding of multiple-choice questions will allow you to most effectively apply your nursing knowledge and skills to the testing situation.

A multiple-choice question is constructed so that only someone who has mastered the subject matter will select the correct answer. To that person, only one option appears to be the correct answer. To someone who lacks a firm grasp of the subject matter, all options look equally attractive and plausible.

Use the Three-Step Approach

It is often helpful to use the following three-step approach to answer the multiple-choice questions that appear on the CRNE.

1. For *case-based* questions, carefully read the information provided in the case text and try to understand the person's health situation and the nursing care the person is likely to require.

2. For *all* questions, read the stem (the question portion) first. Before looking at the options, make sure you have understood what the question is asking. Use the information provided and, based on your nursing knowledge and skills, try to formulate the correct answer.

3. Study all the options provided and select the one that comes closest to the answer you formulated or the one that is the best option of the alternatives given. You may wish to reread the stem before finalizing your selection.

Take Advantage of the Process of Elimination

After reading the stem of the question, if you do not see an option that matches or is close to the one you expected, try to eliminate some of the options that are absolutely incorrect. The following example illustrates how you can benefit from the process of elimination.

Question

Which response by the nurse would best assist Mrs. Clement to verbalize her fears when she expresses anxiety about the possibility of having a mastectomy?

1. State that the nurse understands how she feels.

2. Ask her to talk to the nurse-in-charge.

3. Validate her concerns regarding the need to have surgery.

4. Explain that it is a normal reaction to fear surgery.

To take full advantage of the process of elimination, it is important to focus on the key idea in the stem. The key idea is assisting Mrs. Clement to verbalize her fears.

In Option 1, the focus is on the nurse and not on Mrs. Clement or her concerns. Option 1 can be eliminated because it is highly unlikely that anyone knows exactly how someone else feels in a given situation.

Option 2 also fails to address Mrs. Clement's immediate concern because the nurse completely avoids dealing with Mrs. Clement and passes the responsibility on to another person. For this reason, Option 2 can be eliminated as a possible correct answer.

Option 4 should also be eliminated immediately. By telling Mrs. Clement that what she is experiencing is "normal," the nurse implies that Mrs. Clement's situation is routine. Such a response would be depersonalizing and non-therapeutic.

After these three options are systematically eliminated, you can consider Option 3, the correct option, which is open ended and encourages Mrs. Clement to begin talking about how she feels about her upcoming surgery.

Checklist of Common Test-Taking Errors

Candidates often make mistakes on an exam because of errors in processing facts and information. These are technical errors related to writing tests, not errors related to a lack of nursing knowledge or skill.

As you complete the practice questions, you may wish to keep a checklist of common test-taking errors you may have made. Tick off the particular technical error(s) you made with the questions you answered incorrectly. Keep in mind that you may have made more than one technical error with any one question.

- Missed important information in the case text

- Misread the stem of the question

- Failed to pick out important or key words in the stem of the question

- Did not relate the question to information in the case text

- Made assumptions in the case text or question

- Focused on insignificant details and missed key issues

- Selected more than one answer

- Incorrectly transferred answer from selection in test booklet to computer answer sheet

- Switched answer selected

- Other (specify) _____
  _____
  _____

CHAPTER 4:
COMPLETING THE PRACTICE QUESTIONS

■ COMPLETING THE PRACTICE QUESTIONS

How you complete the practice questions will depend on whether you are using method A, B or C (described in chapter 1). If you plan to complete the practice questions only once, it is best to simulate the actual examination conditions as closely as possible. This means completing the questions in a quiet location, without the benefit of books, notes or other aids, and strictly adhering to the time limit (four hours).

INSTRUCTIONS

In order for you to become familiar with the CRNE format, the front cover and the instructions that are included here are very similar to those that appear on the CRNE. The front cover contains a test form number that is also repeated in the lower left-hand corner of each page of the CRNE. This test form number is required for scoring the CRNE.

Answering the questions using the blank answer sheets, included at the back of the prep guide, will help you gain experience in recording the personal information and filling in the ovals that correspond to your answer selections. If you are using the CD-ROM, you simply click the bubble beside the option.

When you have finished all the questions, you can calculate your total score and create your performance profile. Instructions for calculating your score and determining your performance profile are provided in chapters 5 and 6.

If you prefer to complete the practice questions using the CD-ROM, your result and performance profile will be generated automatically once you have completed the questions. You can also transfer your results from the answer sheet to the CD-ROM. The computer will then calculate your results automatically and produce a performance profile.

TEST FORM 0101101
CANADIAN REGISTERED NURSE EXAMINATION

IMPORTANT NOTICE

This test booklet and its contents, including the exam questions, are highly confidential and are the property of the Canadian Nurses Association. Candidates taking the exam are therefore prohibited from disclosing the contents of the test booklet and must not, under any circumstances, share any of the information it contains with any person, except as authorized by the Canadian Nurses Association. Unauthorized production, reproduction or publication of the exam questions is also prohibited by copyright laws. In addition, the Canadian Nurses Association has implemented measures and statistical procedures to detect cheating (i.e., copying answers from another candidate; voluntarily or involuntarily providing answers to another candidate). Unauthorized disclosure of the contents of the test booklet and any other form of cheating is unethical behaviour and shall result in sanctions. If the regulatory authority determines that a candidate has cheated on the exam, the candidate is automatically assigned a fail result and the writing is counted as an exam writing. Other sanctions may be imposed and may extend to being denied access into the profession.

CANDIDATE DECLARATION

I acknowledge that I have read the above provisions regarding the disclosure, production, reproduction or publication of the test booklet and its contents, and cheating with respect to the examination. My signature on this test booklet constitutes my agreement not to disclose, produce, reproduce or otherwise engage in the publication of the test booklet and its contents, unless authorized by the Canadian Nurses Association, or to cheat with respect to the examination.

				–				

CANDIDATE NUMBER

_____

PRINT NAME

_____

SIGNATURE

READ THE INSTRUCTIONS AND SAMPLE QUESTIONS INSIDE THE FRONT COVER

A product of the Canadian Nurses Association CNA

INSTRUCTIONS

(NOTE: THE FOLLOWING ARE INSTRUCTIONS YOU WILL RECEIVE WHEN TAKING THE CRNE.)

A) TESTING TIME AND MATERIAL

You will have four hours to complete the CRNE. The starting and finishing times will be announced, and you will be advised when there are 30 and 15 minutes working time remaining. If at any time you have any questions about what you should do, raise your hand and an invigilator will assist you.

Clear your desk of all materials except your identification card, answer sheet, test booklet, pencils and eraser. **Do not fold, bend or tear your answer sheet, as this could affect the scoring of your exam.**

You will be advised whether you may leave the examination room if you finish the test before the time is up. You must stop working when the signal is given. An invigilator will check your test booklet and answer sheet before you leave.

B) ANSWER SHEET

Complete the identification portion of your answer sheet:

• Print your name, date of birth and date of the exam.

• Print and fill in the seven-digit test form number (from the cover of your test booklet).

If you have a candidate label provided with your identification card:

• Detach the label from the identification card and place the label in the appropriate location on the answer sheet.

• **DO NOT** fill in the information to the right of the candidate label unless the candidate label is incorrect.

If you DO NOT have a candidate label:

• Fill in the oval corresponding to the language of writing.

• Print your candidate number and writing centre code AND fill the corresponding oval for each digit.

Be sure the mark you make for each answer is black, fills the oval and contains the number corresponding to the number of the answer you have chosen.

Do not fill in more than one oval for a question or you will get no credit for it.

Erase **completely** any answer you wish to change and mark your new choice in the correct oval. An incomplete erasure may be read incorrectly as an intended answer.

Do not press too heavily on your pencil or you may damage the answer sheet. Make no stray marks on the answer sheet; they may count against you.

Note that the questions on the answer sheet are numbered in columns. There are fewer questions in the test booklet than there are numbers on the answer sheet.

You may use the margins of the test booklet for any scratch work, but you will not get credit for anything you write in the test booklet.

C) TEST BOOKLET

Print AND sign your name on the lines on the cover of this test booklet and copy your candidate number into the appropriate boxes.

Read each question carefully and choose the answer that you think is the best. If you cannot decide on an answer to a question, go on to the next one and come back to this question later if you have time. Try to answer all questions. Marks are not subtracted for wrong answers. If you are not sure of an answer, it will be to your advantage to guess. It will probably be best to start at the beginning of the test and work through the questions in order.

This exam contains a number of experimental questions being tested for future use. Your answers to these questions will not count toward your score. Because you will not be able to tell which questions are experimental, you should do your best on all questions, but do not spend too much time on any one question.

The questions on the exam are presented as cases or as independent questions. The context of some cases may seem similar to others in your test booklet. This reflects current practice where a registered nurse may have to care for different persons with similar problems. Each case, however, tests different nursing content. The sample case on the next page shows the types of questions used. Correct answers are blackened in the ovals below the question.

■ SAMPLE CASE

Mr. St-Dennis, 78 years old, has returned to the surgical unit following a left total hip replacement.

QUESTIONS 1 to 5 refer to this case.

---

1. Upon return to the unit, Mr. St-Dennis' vital signs are BP 90/60, HR 58, RR 14, T 36.1 °C, and oxygen saturation is 96%. He seems surprised when he sees his blood pressure reading. How should the nurse respond?

    1. Reassure him that his vital signs are stable and there is nothing to worry about.
    2. Notify the physician about his low blood pressure and heart rate.
    3. Inform him that his heart rate and blood pressure are too low, and the physician will be informed.
    4. Ask him about his usual blood pressure range and check records for preoperative vital signs.

---

2. Several hours later, the nurse plans to teach Mr. St-Dennis how to prevent respiratory complications following surgery. What should the nurse do?

    1. Instruct him to take several slow, deep breaths every hour to promote lung expansion.
    2. Inform him that oxygen will be administered if oxygen saturations fall below normal range.
    3. Advise him to sit in the orthopneic position to promote optimal lung expansion.
    4. Ask him what he has been taught regarding deep breathing exercises following surgery.

---

3. Mr. St-Dennis asks the nurse if there are any mobility or positioning restrictions following surgery. How should the nurse respond?

    1. There are no mobility or positioning restrictions following this surgical procedure.
    2. Avoid abducting legs and full weight-bearing when ambulating.
    3. Refrain from crossing legs and flexing hips more than 90 degrees.
    4. Limit sitting up in the chair or side lying to 20 minutes.

---

4. One day after surgery, the nurse informs Mr. St-Dennis that he will be ambulating with the physiotherapist. Mr. St-Dennis says it would be better if he rested in bed because he has a lot of pain when he moves. How should the nurse respond?

   1. Respect the client's choice to rest in bed.

   2. Explain the importance of early ambulation following surgery.

   3. Inform the client that according to the physician's orders, he must ambulate today.

   4. Teach the client relaxation exercises and visual imagery to reduce pain during ambulation.

5. Later that day, Mr. St-Dennis reports that he feels short of breath and fatigued. Vital signs are BP 128/70, HR 92, RR 30, and oxygen saturation is 96% while on oxygen at 3 L/min. The nurse auscultates crackles up to the mid-lung fields bilaterally and observes +2 pitting edema to the lower legs. What should the nurse do?

   1. Assure the client that it is normal to feel fatigued following major surgery and encourage deep breathing exercises.

   2. Provide the client with an incentive spirometer and encourage him to use it on an hourly basis.

   3. Inform the physician about changes in the client's condition and request orders.

   4. Contact the physician to request orders to increase oxygen and administer a bronchodilator.

END OF SAMPLE CASE

DO NOT OPEN YOUR TEST BOOKLET OR BEGIN WORKING UNTIL INSTRUCTED TO DO SO.

■ CASE 1

Ms. Rankin, 25 years old, and Mr. McKay, 26 years old, are expecting their first baby. They are interested to learn more about the pregnancy and infant care.

QUESTIONS 1 to 5 refer to this case.

1. Ms. Rankin and Mr. McKay enrol in group prenatal education sessions. When facilitating the classes, how can the public health nurse best convey information?

    1. Deliver a PowerPoint presentation.
    2. Use familiar objects as teaching aids.
    3. Explain pain control methods in labour and delivery.
    4. Write a list of fears about labour and delivery.

2. Mr. McKay visits the public health nurse stating that he wants to support his partner but does not feel confident assisting her in labour and delivery. What would be the most appropriate nursing response?

    1. Have Mr. McKay practise comfort measures for labour and delivery.
    2. Ask the labour and delivery nurses to make Mr. McKay feel welcome upon arrival.
    3. Inform Mr. McKay that it is his right to choose to be present during labour and delivery.
    4. Give Mr. McKay an infant care video so he can help with the baby after delivery.

3. Ms. Rankin sees the public health nurse at 1 week postpartum for a routine visit. What information provided by Ms. Rankin would cause the nurse to be concerned?

    1. Seven wet diapers per 24 hours
    2. Breastfeeding every 6 hours
    3. Mustard-coloured bowel movement
    4. Nursing from one breast per feeding

4. The couple have decided to wean 6-week-old Jacey to commercial formula. Which action would support their decision?

    1. Inform the couple that formula is not the best nutrition for their baby.
    2. Advise Ms. Rankin to discuss this issue with her physician.
    3. Offer a breastfeeding information video for the couple to take home.
    4. Discuss proper preparation and technique for formula feeding.

5. Ms. Rankin and Mr. McKay express stress regarding the transition to being new parents. What should the public health nurse suggest to assist the couple during this transitional period?

    1. Support group for new parents

    2. Equal sharing of infant care

    3. Ms. Rankin's mother to visit

    4. Adjustments to parenthood take time

END OF CASE 1

■ CASE 2

Mr. Parker, 52 years old, is 175 cm tall, weighs 110 kg, and has type 1 diabetes. He tells the nurse that he is in a high-pressure sales position, has difficulty sleeping and often eats fast food. He is divorced and enjoys spending time with his two children monthly.

QUESTIONS 6 to 9 refer to this case.

6. Mr. Parker is brought to the emergency department with a headache and drowsiness. He is diaphoretic and states that his heart is racing. His blood glucose is 2.2 mmol/L. What should the nurse do first?

    1. Report the results to the physician.

    2. Discuss the need to lose weight.

    3. Administer fast-acting carbohydrates.

    4. Explain how to treat low blood glucose.

7. What places Mr. Parker at the most significant risk for hypertension?

    1. Hypoglycemia

    2. Stress

    3. Visiting his two children

    4. Eating fast food

8. How can the nurse best assist Mr. Parker in managing his diabetes?

    1. Advise him to visit his family physician.

    2. Suggest that he change jobs.

    3. Encourage him to see a dietitian.

    4. Refer him to a counsellor.

9. What is the most appropriate teaching approach for Mr. Parker?

    1. Telling
    2. Discovery
    3. Participating
    4. Lecture

END OF CASE 2

■ CASE 3

Mrs. Thompson, 41 years old, is a married mother of three children and has chronic fatigue syndrome. She is referred to the community health nurse for assistance with performing activities of daily living (ADLs).

QUESTIONS 10 to 14 refer to this case.

10. During the initial home visit, the nurse assesses Mrs. Thompson's ability to perform ADLs. Mrs. Thompson states that at times she overexerts herself and then is unable to get out of bed the next day. What should the nurse suggest to Mrs. Thompson?

    1. Design a chart with a list of daily and weekly activities.
    2. Balance rest and activity.
    3. Identify tasks that can be delegated.
    4. Increase the level of activity through passive exercises.

11. The nurse has never provided care for a client living with chronic fatigue syndrome. What should the nurse do first?

    1. Develop a comprehensive client and family care plan.
    2. Research the literature on chronic fatigue syndrome.
    3. Identify areas requiring further assessment of the client and family.
    4. Review the physician's referral notes to learn more about the client.

12. What is the most important aspect for the nurse to teach Mrs. Thompson about the problem-solving process?

    1. Setting small achievable goals
    2. Establishing priorities
    3. Creating an evaluation plan
    4. Identifying delegated tasks

13.   Mrs. Thompson says that she feels guilty because her husband has to do housework, prepare meals and care for their children. What should the nurse do first?

    1.   Ask Mrs. Thompson's friends and family to assist with chores.

    2.   Teach Mrs. Thompson energy conservation techniques.

    3.   Refer the family to a social worker.

    4.   Conduct a family meeting.

14.   The nurse notes a change in Mrs. Thompson's thoughts and behaviour. What should the nurse assess to determine the risk of suicide?

    1.   Feelings of despair, guilt and excessive sleeping

    2.   Social isolation, sleep disturbance and feelings of hopelessness

    3.   Anxiety, inattention to personal hygiene and fear

    4.   Limited insight, loss of personal control and poor judgment

END OF CASE 3

■ CASE 4

Mrs. Chadra, 36 years old, gravida 2, is 3 days postpartum following a vacuum-assisted vaginal delivery of a live female infant of 38 weeks gestation. Mrs. Chadra's blood type is A, Rh-negative, and the infant's blood type is O, Rh-positive. Prenatal blood work shows that Mrs. Chadra had been previously sensitized. Antibody titres were done frequently during her pregnancy.

QUESTIONS 15 to 17 refer to this case.

15.   A nursing student asks for assistance with understanding Rh incompatibility and Rh antiglobulin administration. What information should the nurse provide to the nursing student?

    1.   Rh serum is given during the antepartum period when the mother is Rh-negative and the mother's indirect Coombs' test is negative.

    2.   Rh-negative women have Rh antigens in their red blood cells, which can cause antibody formation when exposed to fetal Rh-positive blood.

    3.   Immunoglobulin M (IgM) antibodies can cause an increase in red blood cell production in the fetus, causing hyperbilirubinemia.

    4.   If Rh immune globulin is given after an amniocentesis and again at 28 weeks, no further dose is required after delivery.

16. Mrs. Chadra's infant has a large bruised area on the back of her head, and there is swelling on one side of her head as a result of the vacuum delivery method. The nurse notes that the swelling does not cross cranial suture lines. What should the nurse conclude from these assessment findings?

    1. The infant is at risk for infection.

    2. The infant is at risk for seizure activity.

    3. The infant has caput succedaneum.

    4. The infant has a cephalhematoma.

17. Mrs. Chadra's infant looks jaundiced, and the physician confirms that some antibodies are attacking the infant's blood. What information should the nurse provide the mother concerning her infant?

    1. Hemolysis can cause jaundice so the infant may need phototherapy.

    2. Exchange transfusion should be anticipated for this infant.

    3. The infant will have a negative antibody test if Rh immune globulin is given during pregnancy.

    4. A blood group and type test is performed on the cord blood for maternal antibodies.

END OF CASE 4

■ CASE 5

Mr. Juliano, 73 years old, has just been admitted to the medical unit with an exacerbation of his chronic congestive heart failure. He states that he is having more trouble breathing today and did not sleep well last night.

QUESTIONS 18 to 22 refer to this case.

18. Mr. Juliano's respirations become laboured. Prior to the physician's arrival, what should the nurse do first?

    1. Place him in high-Fowler's position.

    2. Start oxygen therapy at a high flow rate.

    3. Prepare the equipment to start an intravenous infusion.

    4. Arrange for the laboratory to draw blood for blood gas analysis.

19. Mr. Juliano is receiving O_2 by Venturi mask. How can the nurse promote a safe environment while this therapy is being carried out?

    1. Replace cotton blankets with polyester ones.

    2. Remove electrical equipment from the room.

    3. Check that the ports on the mask are unobstructed.

    4. Avoid using oil-based creams when providing skin care.

20.   Mr. Juliano is receiving digoxin (Lanoxin). What must the nurse assess prior to giving the medication?

1. Heart rate

2. Blood pressure

3. Respiratory rate

4. Level of activity

21.   On the third day following Mr. Juliano's admission, what observation would be the most important to include in the report to the incoming shift of nursing staff?

1. His weight continues to remain stable.

2. He is dizzy when he first gets out of bed.

3. He needs reminders to keep his feet elevated.

4. He has been sleeping short periods at regular intervals.

22.   What factor would contribute most to Mr. Juliano experiencing sensory overload?

1. His intravenous rate is checked hourly.

2. His wife visits each afternoon.

3. Drapes are drawn to block strong sunlight.

4. Oxygen humidification unit bubbles continuously.

END OF CASE 5

■ CASE 6

Mrs. Kenny, 55 years old, was diagnosed 15 years ago with type 2 diabetes. She has been taking the maximum dose of metformin (Glucophage) and glyburide (Diabeta) to manage her diabetes. She visits the community health nurse.

QUESTIONS 23 to 26 refer to this case.

23.   During a visit, Mrs. Kenny indicates that she does not understand the importance of examining her feet. What should the nurse do?

1. Discuss with Mrs. Kenny how foot problems can be prevented with proper foot care and glycemic control.

2. Suggest that Mrs. Kenny attend education classes for more information on diabetes complications.

3. Provide Mrs. Kenny with research articles concerning type 2 diabetes.

4. Refer Mrs. Kenny to information she received when she was first diagnosed.

24. Mrs. Kenny indicates that she occasionally drinks a can of cola when she is thirsty. What should the nurse do?

    1. Tell her to drink diet cola instead.

    2. Have her avoid drinking regular cola.

    3. Explore with her whether cola is the best choice.

    4. Provide her with a list of beverages that will not raise blood sugars.

25. On the basis of the laboratory results and home blood glucose reading, Mrs. Kenny should start on insulin. How should the nurse communicate this information to Mrs. Kenny's physician?

    1. Ask Mrs. Kenny to make a follow-up appointment with her physician.

    2. Discuss with the physician Mrs. Kenny's visit and that insulin was initiated.

    3. Send a report to the physician about Mrs. Kenny's visit and blood-work results.

    4. Call Mrs. Kenny's physician and schedule an appointment for her.

26. During the teaching session on insulin administration, Mrs. Kenny indicates that she wants to use only her abdomen for insulin injections. What should the nurse do?

    1. Advise her that many people prefer to use their abdomen initially and, as her comfort level increases, other areas should be considered.

    2. Inform Mrs. Kenny that using only her abdomen will increase her risk for scar tissue buildup, which affects insulin absorption.

    3. Educate Mrs. Kenny that it is common for people to want to use their abdomen, but she needs to rotate sites from the beginning.

    4. Review with her the sites for injection again, because she may not have understood the information when it was presented.

END OF CASE 6

■ CASE 7

Mr. Chartrand, 67 years old, has a history of chronic obstructive pulmonary disease (COPD). He is admitted with right lower lobe pneumonia. He appears tired, anxious and dyspneic. His vital signs are HR 88, BP 140/80, RR 20, T 38.1 °C per axilla, and his SpO_2 is 88% on 2 L/min by nasal cannula. He is accompanied by his wife.

QUESTIONS 27 to 31 refer to this case.

27. What immediate action should the nurse take when Mr. Chartrand is admitted to his room?

    1. Ask Mrs. Chartrand to go to the waiting room.

    2. Place Mr. Chartrand in a high-Fowler's position with arms supported.

    3. Complete a thorough health history on Mr. Chartrand.

    4. Increase Mr. Chartrand's oxygen to 4 L/min.

28. Mr. Chartrand has difficulty sleeping and he requests a sedative, since he was taking one at home. What should the nurse do?

    1. Call his physician to obtain an order for a sedative.

    2. Teach him relaxation techniques.

    3. Increase his oxygen concentration.

    4. Refer him to an anxiety disorders clinic.

29. Mr. Chartrand's pneumonia has resolved. He wants to know how he can cope better at home. What should the nurse do?

    1. Instruct him to take even breaths in and out while he leans forward against the wall.

    2. Teach him huff coughing techniques so that CO_2 will not be trapped in his airways.

    3. Ask him what strategies he has been using to deal with his COPD at home.

    4. Tell him to attend a pulmonary rehabilitation program.

30. Mr. Chartrand has a history of smoking one pack of cigarettes per day for the past 40 years. He expresses a desire to quit and has concerns about dealing with withdrawal. How should the nurse respond?

    1. Nicotine withdrawal is mostly related to physical dependence and withdrawal symptoms last about 48 hours.

    2. His nutritional status will improve as a result of the increased appetite that occurs with withdrawal.

    3. Since his wife has quit successfully, she will be able to provide support for him.

    4. There are medications and cessation programs available to help reduce the cravings associated with withdrawal.

31. Mr. Chartrand was diagnosed with cor pulmonale due to COPD. What information should the nurse provide?

   1. COPD has caused enlargement of the right side of the heart.

   2. These are the symptoms of left-sided heart failure.

   3. COPD has led to an inflammation in his heart muscle.

   4. A blood clot has blocked a blood vessel in his lung.

END OF CASE 7

■ CASE 8

Pandemic influenza has been identified in Indonesia and all health-care facilities are on high alert.

QUESTIONS 32 to 35 refer to this case.

32. Which measures demonstrate knowledge of required precautions for pandemic influenza?

   1. Wearing gloves, gown and a mask whenever in a client's room

   2. Wearing a mask, gloves and gown within 1 metre of a client

   3. Wearing gloves, gown and a mask only if providing personal care to a client

   4. Wearing a mask whenever on an affected unit, and gloves and gown only with anticipated contact

33. What information should the nurse know regarding hand hygiene?

   1. Handwashing is more effective for hand hygiene than alcohol-based hand sanitizers.

   2. Handwashing is a better choice than an alcohol-based hand sanitizer because it will preserve the integrity of the skin on hands.

   3. Alcohol-based hand sanitizers are safe, effective alternatives to handwashing if hands are not visibly soiled.

   4. Alcohol-based hand sanitizers should not be used because they are ineffective against spores.

34. As a result of the outbreak, the housekeeping department is unable to continue with all services on a closed dementia unit because of low staffing levels. What should the nurse do?

   1. Utilize volunteers to assist residents on the unit.

   2. Place the entire dementia unit on isolation.

   3. Ask families of well residents to take their family members home.

   4. Move the well residents to another unit.

35. The outbreak is declared over. During the debriefing, some nursing staff express anger over management of the outbreak. How should the nurse manager respond?

1. State that everyone makes poor decisions at times.

2. Balance the conversation with examples of positive outcomes.

3. Suggest a time for a review of the outbreak.

4. Ask the infection control nurse to resolve the issues.

END OF CASE 8

■ CASE 9

Ms. Pinchant, 56 years old, is admitted to the surgical unit with a diagnosis of acute bowel obstruction. History reveals abdominal pain and vomiting for 3 days. An IV of 1,000 mL of normal saline is infusing, and a nasogastric (Salem sump) tube is attached to intermittent suction.

QUESTIONS 36 to 40 refer to this case.

36. Ms. Pinchant's arterial blood gas results are pH 7.42; PCO_2 47 mmHg; HCO_3^- 34 mmol/L; PO_2 85 mmHg. What do these results indicate?

1. Respiratory acidosis

2. Metabolic acidosis

3. Respiratory alkalosis

4. Metabolic alkalosis

37. On initial rounds, the nurse discovers that there is brown drainage backing up through the blue pigtail of the nasogastric tube. What should be the priority action?

1. Remove and replace the nasogastric tube.

2. Clamp the blue pigtail with forceps.

3. Position the blue pigtail above the client's waist.

4. Irrigate the blue pigtail with normal saline.

38. Ms. Pinchant has just learned that she will require a colostomy. She is sobbing and indicates that this will ruin her marriage and her social life. What is the most appropriate way for the nurse to respond?

1. Refer Ms. Pinchant to a hospital psychologist to discuss her concerns.

2. Ask Ms. Pinchant if she might like a visit from someone who is living successfully with a colostomy.

3. Tell Ms. Pinchant about the local ostomy support group and suggest that she attend regular meetings.

4. Assure Ms. Pinchant that her husband will be supportive and that her life will not change significantly.

39. Following surgery, initial assessment reveals that the stoma is pink with slight sanguineous drainage. Two hours later, one side of the stoma appears dusky blue. What should be the priority action?

    1. Reassess the stoma in 2 hours.
    2. Chart the information in the nursing notes.
    3. Notify the surgeon of this assessment finding.
    4. Apply a moist saline compress to the stoma immediately.

40. The nurse offers to assist a nursing student with changing Ms. Pinchant's colostomy appliance. The student indicates reluctance to take on the procedure. What should be the initial approach by the nurse?

    1. Provide assurance that the student will not be alone and assistance will be provided if needed.
    2. Acknowledge that this is an unpleasant procedure and reassure the student that it will not be as unpleasant as anticipated.
    3. Explain to the student that, as professionals, nurses are required to learn new procedures.
    4. Explore the reasons why the student is reluctant to undertake the procedure.

END OF CASE 9

■ CASE 10

Mr. James, 45 years old, has returned to a surgical unit following a hiatus hernia repair. His chart states that he is moderately developmentally challenged.

QUESTIONS 41 to 45 refer to this case.

41. The nurse assesses Mr. James and decides to administer dimenhydrinate (Gravol) 25 mg IM, which the physician has ordered to be administered q.4h p.r.n. This drug is dispensed in 5 mL vials containing 250 mg. What would be the correct volume for the nurse to administer to Mr. James?

    1. 0.05 mL
    2. 0.25 mL
    3. 0.50 mL
    4. 2.50 mL

42. Mr. James has a #16 indwelling urinary catheter in place. The nurse notes that there has been 35 mL of urinary output in the past hour whereas the previous hourly rate had been approximately 70 mL. What should the nurse do first?

    1. Remove the catheter and replace it with one of a larger size.
    2. Irrigate the catheter using a large volume syringe and sterile solution.
    3. Disconnect the catheter from the drainage bag to check for urinary flow.
    4. Check the catheter and drainage tubing for kinks that might impede flow.

43. Following surgery, Mr. James is to receive three units of packed red blood cells. What should the nurse do?

   1. Ensure that the transfusion is maintained at a constant flow rate.

   2. Regulate the infusion to the slowest possible rate to avoid transfusion reactions.

   3. Infuse the blood slowly for the first 15 minutes and then increase the flow rate to that ordered by the physician.

   4. Administer the transfusion as quickly as possible by using a pressure appliance on each unit of packed red blood cells.

44. What nursing action would best ensure Mr. James' safety?

   1. Have a relative remain with him.

   2. Supervise him when he performs activities.

   3. Move his bed closer to the nurses' station.

   4. Place a sign above his bed indicating to the staff that he needs special supervision.

45. Postoperatively, Mr. James has been having small, liquid bowel movements frequently. The nurse assesses that he has a large amount of hard feces in his rectum. What should the nurse do?

   1. Request an order for a saline enema.

   2. Administer the prescribed laxative every night.

   3. Ask him what method he usually uses to correct constipation.

   4. Insert a lubricated, gloved finger into the rectum and break up the fecal mass.

END OF CASE 10

■ CASE 11

Mrs. Wylder, 21 years old, is admitted at 23:00 to the surgical ward with abdominal pain. The physician orders Mrs. Wylder to be n.p.o., a complete blood count and an ultrasound in the morning. Vital signs on admission are: HR 80, RR 18 and BP 117/78. She began spotting 2 days ago and her last normal menstrual period was 5 weeks ago.

QUESTIONS 46 to 49 refer to this case.

46. At 02:00, Mrs. Wylder is vomiting, diaphoretic and reporting excruciating abdominal pain. Her vital signs are HR 115, RR 24 and BP 98/72. She is prepared for emergency laparoscopic surgery. What should be the nurse's priority action?

   1. Administer pain medication as ordered.

   2. Call the client's spouse.

   3. Call the ultrasound technician stat.

   4. Have the client's blood typed and crossmatched.

47. The client is expected in the operating room in 30 minutes. The nurse has not completed the admission documentation. What is the best way for the nurse to communicate the client's information to the perioperative nurse?

    1. Telephone the report to the operating room.

    2. Complete each entry of the perioperative checklist.

    3. Add the nursing history and medication sheet to the chart.

    4. Include the nursing care plan in the transferred information.

48. Following surgery for a ruptured fallopian tube, Ms. Wylder returns to the surgical ward at 08:30. The surgeon orders one unit of packed red blood cells. What should be the nurse's priority action?

    1. Take the client's temperature, pulse, respirations and oxygen saturation.

    2. Check to see if the client has a patent intravenous line.

    3. Ensure that the client's blood sample has been crossed and typed within the past 72 hours.

    4. Read through the client's chart to determine the blood type.

49. During the blood transfusion, Mr. Wylder asks the nurse to explain why his wife lost the baby. How should the nurse best respond?

    1. Tell Mr. Wylder that this is not a good time for discussion.

    2. Explain that ectopic pregnancy is a fertilized ovum implanted in the wrong place.

    3. Tell him that ectopic pregnancies are caused by repeated pelvic infection.

    4. Validate Mr. Wylder's concerns and arrange to speak with him and his wife.

END OF CASE 11

■ CASE 12

Emma, 8 weeks old, is admitted to the pediatric unit with respiratory distress. Her mother accompanies her. Emma's vital signs are HR 172, RR 44, T 39 °C axillary. Her chest has expiratory wheezes with decreased air entry to the lobes bilaterally and mild intercostal and subcostal indrawing.

QUESTIONS 50 to 53 refer to this case.

50. Emma's mother asks to hang garlic around Emma's neck because she believes this will help Emma get better. What should be the nurse's best response?

    1. State that hanging garlic around a child's neck puts the child at risk for strangulation.

    2. Ask the mother if this practice is a family tradition when someone is sick.

    3. Inform the mother that hospital policy does not allow hanging things around a child's neck.

    4. Discuss the treatment ordered for Emma with the mother.

51.   The nurse observes that Emma's respiratory effort has become more laboured with moderate accessory muscle use. She also takes longer to settle between hourly checks. What would minimize her distress during assessments?

1.   Conduct respiratory assessment while Emma is asleep.

2.   Spread personal care activities throughout the day.

3.   Position Emma on her side for sleep.

4.   Keep lights off.

52.   The nurse reassesses Emma after salbutamol (Ventolin) administration. Emma's HR is 190, RR 52, T 38 °C axillary. Emma's chest has decreased wheezes with slightly decreased air entry to the lobes bilaterally. Emma is extremely restless and has tremors. What should the nurse suspect is happening with Emma?

1.   Condition is worsening due to her fever.

2.   Her vital signs reflect a slight fever.

3.   Change is in response to the medication.

4.   Restlessness is expected with a respiratory infection.

53.   As the shift progresses, Michael, a 4-week-old infant, is admitted with respiratory distress and dehydration. The nurse now has five clients. Michael appears to be in severe distress and dehydrated. What can the nurse do to manage this workload?

1.   Move Michael and Emma into the same room.

2.   Assign tasks to other staff members.

3.   Report the workload to the union or other regulatory body.

4.   Manage the workload as best as possible until the next shift.

END OF CASE 12

■ CASE 13

Mrs. Kirsh, 70 years old, has been admitted to hospital with acute renal failure. She is in the oliguric phase and reports nausea and drowsiness.

QUESTIONS 54 to 59 refer to this case.

54.   Mrs. Kirsh's urine specific gravity is low. Laboratory data reveal hyponatremia and hyperkalemia. What assessment should the nurse conduct?

1.   Listen to her chest.

2.   Note signs of hypovolemia.

3.   Observe for postural hypotension.

4.   Assess for signs of fluid volume deficit.

55. What is the nursing priority when planning care for Mrs. Kirsh?

   1. Encourage oral fluid intake.

   2. Weigh the client before meals.

   3. Leave the side rails up at all times.

   4. Support independence in activities of daily living.

56. What nursing intervention is a priority to be performed hourly?

   1. Turn and position.

   2. Measure urinary output.

   3. Promote deep breathing.

   4. Check for signs of edema.

57. The nurse answers Mrs. Kirsh's call light to find her looking very agitated and exclaiming, "Nurse, look what's happened. Am I bleeding to death?" She is holding a kidney basin with approximately 60 mL of bloody emesis. What should the nurse do first?

   1. Call the physician.

   2. Ask her what she did.

   3. Validate her feelings.

   4. Indicate that this is normal.

58. A float nurse, unfamiliar with the unit, is assigned to care for Mrs. Kirsh. What should the nurse-in-charge do to ensure that any noticeable changes in Mrs. Kirsh's condition are reported?

   1. Check the float nurse's charting.

   2. Verify the float nurse's assessment.

   3. Review with the float nurse what should be assessed and reported.

   4. Ask the nurse working in the next room to be available to the float nurse.

59. Mrs. Kirsh has been making satisfactory progress and her IV has been discontinued. What intervention should the nurse take to ensure that Mrs. Kirsh's food and fluid needs will continue to be met?

   1. Provide milkshakes t.i.d.

   2. Ensure her privacy during meals.

   3. Encourage a high-calorie breakfast.

   4. Measure her intake and output.

END OF CASE 13

■ CASE 14

Kyle, 14 years old, has been referred to an outpatient clinic because of suicidal ideations. He lives with his mother, who is single.

QUESTIONS 60 to 65 refer to this case.

---

60. Kyle states to the nurse, "I'm not talking to you. You're just like all the other grown-ups who keep bugging me." How should the nurse respond?

    1. "Do you feel like other adults are against you?"

    2. "I would like to hear more about what you are feeling."

    3. "I will be happy to come back when you feel like talking."

    4. "How can you know that I will be like other grown-ups in your life?"

---

61. An interview with Kyle reveals that he is a classmate of the nurse's son, David. What should the nurse do to ensure confidentiality?

    1. Refrain from discussing any aspect of Kyle's care with David.

    2. Inform the health-care team that another nurse should care for Kyle.

    3. Ask David not to discuss Kyle's suicidal behaviours with his classmates.

    4. Report to Kyle's principal, in confidence, that Kyle is making good progress.

---

62. What should the nurse do when Kyle refuses to attend his prescribed group therapy sessions?

    1. Encourage Kyle to verbalize his reasons for refusing to attend group therapy.

    2. Discuss Kyle's refusal with his mother and solicit her help to encourage him to attend.

    3. Inform Kyle that it is in his best interest to comply with the prescribed treatment plan.

    4. Tell Kyle that he would enjoy the special activity the group has planned for today.

---

63. What should the nurse do when several colleagues suggest that Kyle's plan of care would be more effective if his mother were more actively involved?

    1. Explore the colleagues' suggestion and consider how to incorporate it into the plan of care.

    2. Listen to the colleagues' suggestion and continue with the health-care team's established plan of care.

    3. Recognize personal weakness in psychiatric nursing skills and seek out learning opportunities to develop these skills.

    4. Explain to the colleagues that Kyle's mother has limited resources and should not be expected to be more involved in his care.

64. Kyle's nurse is going on vacation. How should the nurse coordinate Kyle's treatment plan to ensure continuity of care?

1. Assure Kyle that the nurses are aware of his needs and are well qualified to help him.

2. Arrange for Kyle to be admitted to hospital during the nurse's absence so that he can be closely monitored.

3. Discuss the treatment plan and the progress made with Kyle, his mother and the health-care team prior to leaving.

4. Validate with Kyle and his mother that they will be able to follow through on the treatment plan during the nurse's absence.

65. How should the nurse determine Kyle's and his mother's level of satisfaction with the nursing care provided?

1. Request that they complete an agency survey regarding client satisfaction.

2. Seek feedback on their satisfaction with the individual nurses at the agency.

3. Collect data from the health-care team and Kyle's mother regarding evidence of suicidal ideation.

4. Upon discharge, determine whether mutually agreed upon goals have been met.

END OF CASE 14

■ CASE 15

Mrs. Peters, 85 years old, is a widow who has been hospitalized following a hip fracture. She is frail and has a poor appetite. Nasogastric feeding is initiated.

QUESTIONS 66 to 70 refer to this case.

66. What initial intervention should the nurse perform before feeding Mrs. Peters via a nasogastric tube?

1. Check for placement of the tube.

2. Place the client in the left lateral position.

3. Change the tubing before each feeding.

4. Instill 60 mL of water through the tube.

67. What nursing intervention would best promote sensory stimulation for Mrs. Peters?

1. Move her to the activity room.

2. Remove photos of family members.

3. Place a clock and calendar in her room.

4. Talk with her while assisting her with her care.

68. Mrs. Peters becomes confused and refuses to allow the nurse to treat her, saying, "Who are you? Leave me alone." How should the nurse revise Mrs. Peters' plan of care?

    1. Monitor her orientation status.

    2. Provide sedation as necessary.

    3. Encourage her to express her concerns.

    4. Encourage her to participate in her plan of care.

69. The nurse finds it increasingly difficult to care for Mrs. Peters. What should the nurse do to cope with feelings of frustration?

    1. Maintain a high level of care at all times.

    2. Decrease the amount of time spent with Mrs. Peters.

    3. Consult a nursing colleague regarding Mrs. Peters' care.

    4. Ask that another nurse assume Mrs. Peters' care.

70. Mrs. Peters' condition worsens and it becomes difficult to maintain a clear airway. The nurse promotes ventilation and respiration by performing oral and nasal suctioning. What intervention indicates a safe suctioning technique?

    1. Suction the oral cavity first.

    2. Suction for as long as necessary.

    3. Insert the catheter without applying suction.

    4. Place the client in a lateral position facing the nurse.

END OF CASE 15

■ CASE 16

In response to a provincial health policy, it is proposed that health committees be created in schools for grades six to eight. The committees will mainly consist of students.

QUESTIONS 71 to 76 refer to this case.

71. How should the nurse prepare in order to create interest among the students in this new initiative?

    1. Find out about the rationale behind this new policy and list the various ways it can impact student health.

    2. Adopt a positive attitude toward this initiative and hold a contest to find a logo for the committee.

    3. Review workload and make time for this new priority in the nurse's schedule.

    4. Focus on the merits of this initiative and conduct a review of similar projects.

72. According to the results of a questionnaire distributed to the students to assess health status, lack of exercise is the first concern among the students. What action would be most appropriate for the school's health committee to take?

   1. Ask the physical education teachers to add a lesson each week for all students.
   2. Encourage the students to participate in a walking activity in the gym during the morning recess.
   3. Organize a conference for parents on the dangers of the lack of physical exercise.
   4. Invite the students to participate in popular physical activities during the lunch recess.

73. The second priority identified by the students is to improve eating habits. What activity is an example of promoting healthy eating?

   1. Creation of a weight loss group for obese students
   2. A conference on the prevention of eating disorders during adolescence
   3. An activity to determine the healthy weight of students
   4. An information session on *Canada's Food Guide*

74. There is a lack of participation in exercise activities by children in special needs classes. Which principle of primary health care applies to this challenge?

   1. Health status
   2. Intersectoral collaboration
   3. Accessibility
   4. Individual adaptation skills

75. The nurse collaborating with the health committee feels overwhelmed by the committee's requests. What should the nurse do to ensure the continuity of this initiative?

   1. Propose to the committee that it reduce its activities for a while.
   2. Suggest that the committee direct some of its requests to community partners.
   3. Submit a request for funding in order to obtain additional resources.
   4. Prioritize the requests and respond to the most urgent.

76. The nurse and the health committee want to assess participants' satisfaction with the program. What method should be used?

   1. Observation of participants' facial expressions during activities
   2. Weight lost by students at the school during the first year of activities
   3. The number of activities organized during the school year
   4. The number of students participating in activities during the first week

END OF CASE 16

■ CASE 17

A community health nurse receives a referral for Mr. Hazelton, 27 years old, in the terminal stages of HIV/AIDS. He has returned to his rural community and is living with his parents and two brothers.

QUESTIONS 77 to 81 refer to this case.

---

77. The community health nurse has never cared for a client with HIV/AIDS. What is the most appropriate action for the nurse to take?

    1. Request that the client be reassigned to a nurse with more experience.

    2. Attend the home visit with a colleague who has visited clients with HIV/AIDS.

    3. Review policies, procedures and texts to increase knowledge.

    4. Identify a list of resources that the library should obtain for all staff.

---

78. What initial data should the nurse gather to support the nursing care plan?

    1. Environmental hazards

    2. Suicide risk

    3. Health assessment

    4. Sexual health history

---

79. During the second home visit, the nurse is introduced to Mr. Hazelton's partner, who will be providing some of the care. The family is upset and does not want the partner in the home. What should the nurse do?

    1. Explain to Mr. Hazelton that having the partner in the home would be disruptive.

    2. Suggest that the partner find accommodation close by.

    3. Facilitate a discussion with Mr. Hazelton and his family about his unique needs.

    4. Advise the family that it is the client's right to have whoever he wants to provide care.

---

80. Mr. Hazelton informs the nurse that he plans to stay at home to die. The family is uncomfortable with this decision. What should the nurse do?

    1. Encourage Mr. Hazelton to reconsider his decision.

    2. Allow the family to express their concerns.

    3. Ask a social worker to arrange a family meeting.

    4. Explore the mother's beliefs about death and dying.

81. A large birthday party has been planned for Mr. Hazelton's father. The family asks the nurse if it is safe to have guests in the house. What should the nurse recommend?

    1. Ensure that guests do not come in contact with Mr. Hazelton.

    2. Remind the client and family about personal health practices and precautions.

    3. Move the party to a local hotel to reduce risk to the guests.

    4. Advise the guests to be immunized prior to the party.

END OF CASE 17

■ CASE 18

Susan, 18 years old, has a complete spinal cord lesion at T1 and a closed-head injury as a result of a diving accident, which happened one week ago. She has remained unconscious since her admission.

QUESTIONS 82 to 86 refer to this case.

82. The nurse and Susan's mother are bathing Susan. Which nursing approach would best promote a helping relationship between the nurse, Susan and her mother?

    1. Address Susan, stating that her mother is there to wash her.

    2. Quietly ask Susan's mother if she is worried about her daughter's recovery.

    3. Clearly and slowly ask Susan to open her eyes for her mother.

    4. Reduce auditory stimulation and whisper when speaking to Susan's mother.

83. Susan has been started on total parenteral nutrition (TPN). During a bag change, the bag containing the solution of amino acids is inadvertently punctured by the spike on the tubing. What should the nurse do to best maintain the TPN infusion?

    1. Tape the hole with sterile, waterproof tape and continue the infusion.

    2. Slow the infusion and wait for a new bag to be delivered from the pharmacy.

    3. Continue the infusion with dextrose 10% until a new bag is available from the pharmacy.

    4. Increase the rate of the lipid infusion until a new bag of amino acids can be administered.

84. What nursing action would be most effective in promoting circulation in Susan's lower limbs?

    1. Applying resting splints to both legs

    2. Flexing and extending the client's ankles q.2h

    3. Administering warm packs to both calves t.i.d.

    4. Elevating the foot of the client's bed 15 cm with a slight knee bend

85.   In managing the physical environment, what should the nurse do to promote safety for Susan?

1.   Keep the lights in Susan's room dimmed.

2.   Ensure that Susan's bed sheets are free of wrinkles.

3.   Turn Susan from prone to supine positions q.2h.

4.   Have the curtains around Susan's bed open at all times.

86.   The nurse is caring for Susan and three other clients with spinal cord injuries. One of the clients becomes unstable and the nurse cannot attend to the other clients. What should the nurse do?

1.   Document the situation and provide a rationale for the decisions made.

2.   Advise the nurse-in-charge of the situation and request assistance on the unit.

3.   Leave the unstable client in a recovery position and proceed to perform care for the other clients.

4.   Delegate the practical nurse to stay with the unstable client while the nurse attends to the other clients.

END OF CASE 18

■ CASE 19

Mr. Ralph, 62 years old, presents to the emergency department with a sudden onset of periorbital swelling, cough, wheezing and pruritus. Mr. Ralph has no known history of allergies. He is accompanied by his wife and son.

QUESTIONS 87 to 90 refer to this case.

87.   What should be the nurse's initial intervention?

1.   Obtain a full nursing history and assessment upon arrival.

2.   Assess the client's airway and breathing pattern.

3.   Notify the physician immediately and prepare the IV.

4.   Check vital signs and oxygen saturation.

88.   The physician orders epinephrine (Adrenalin) 0.3 mg subcutaneous. The medication comes in a vial of 30 mg in 10 mL (1:1000). How many millilitres should the nurse administer?

1.   0.1 mL

2.   0.3 mL

3.   1 mL

4.   3 mL

89. Following administration of epinephrine (Adrenalin), Mr. Ralph suddenly experiences tremors and restlessness. What is the most appropriate nursing action?

   1. Reassure the client and family that this is a normal side effect of epinephrine.

   2. Inform the physician immediately of the change in the client's condition.

   3. Explain to the client and his family that his condition is deteriorating.

   4. Document the abnormal side effects that the client is experiencing.

90. Upon discharge, the physician prescribes an EpiPen for Mr. Ralph. What discharge teaching would be the most important at this time?

   1. Ensure that the client and his family can demonstrate use of the EpiPen.

   2. Direct the client to go to the emergency department if he experiences a repeat episode.

   3. Instruct the client to keep his EpiPen with him at all times.

   4. Encourage the client to follow up with his family physician regarding allergy testing.

END OF CASE 19

■ CASE 20

Paul, 4 months old, 4.9 kg, is brought to the nursing station with dyspnea, decreased air entry and a harsh, choky cough. Resting vital signs are HR 140, RR 40, BP 78/50, T 38 °C. During feedings, the nurse notices increased respiratory distress. A nasogastric (NG) tube is inserted, and placement is confirmed via chest X-ray.

QUESTIONS 91 to 94 refer to this case.

91. The physician orders acetaminophen (Tylenol) 15 mg/kg p.o. (73.5 mg) every 4 hours p.r.n. for fever. Why should the nurse question the order?

   1. Wrong time

   2. Wrong dose

   3. Wrong drug

   4. Wrong route

92. The nurse suspects that the NG tube is displaced. According to evidence-informed decision-making, what would be the best way to confirm placement at this point?

   1. Use a pH strip and confirm colour of aspirate.

   2. Use the auscultation method of confirmation.

   3. Have another X-ray performed.

   4. Advance the NG tube.

93. The nurse notices that Paul's NG tube has been dislodged on three separate occasions. On the fourth visit to Paul's room, the nurse witnesses Paul's mother pulling out the NG tube. The mother states, "Paul has pulled the tube out again." What is the nursing priority?

   1. Report the situation to the physician.

   2. Initiate protocols to protect Paul from immediate harm.

   3. Place mittens on Paul to prevent him from removing the tube.

   4. Chart the situation on Paul's chart.

94. Paul appears to be getting tired. His vital signs are HR 160, RR 52 with increased accessory muscle use, T 37.5 °C, and BP remains the same. The nurse is concerned about Paul's well-being and is unsure what to do. What is the most appropriate nursing action?

   1. Ask Paul's mother to cuddle him to encourage rest.

   2. Report the findings to the nurse-in-charge and ask for help.

   3. Continue to follow the physician's orders and monitor for improvement.

   4. Ask a more experienced nurse to assume responsibility for Paul.

END OF CASE 20

■ CASE 21

Mr. Brown, 76 years old, is admitted to the medical unit with chronic renal failure.

QUESTIONS 95 to 99 refer to this case.

95. Which manifestation would Mr. Brown exhibit?

   1. Slow, shallow respirations

   2. Fatigue

   3. Hypotension

   4. Cool, clammy skin

96. Mr. Brown has blood gases drawn. The results are pH 7.32, PCO_2 38 mmHg, HCO_3^- 18 mmol/L. What acid-base imbalance is present?

   1. Respiratory acidosis

   2. Respiratory alkalosis

   3. Metabolic acidosis

   4. Metabolic alkalosis

97. Mr. Brown is ordered IV normal saline to infuse at 50 mL/h. The drop factor of the infusion set is 10 gtt/mL. At how many drops per minute should the IV infuse?

1. 8
2. 12
3. 17
4. 21

98. What dietary measures should the nurse implement when caring for Mr. Brown?

1. Decrease fluids and increase protein.
2. Increase fluids and decrease protein.
3. Increase fluids and decrease carbohydrates.
4. Decrease fluids and increase carbohydrates.

99. While his family is visiting, Mr. Brown becomes agitated and attempts to climb out of bed. What should the nurse do first?

1. Encourage the family to sit with Mr. Brown.
2. Obtain an order for physical restraints.
3. Place Mr. Brown in a room near the nurses' station.
4. Ask the physician to prescribe an anti-anxiety agent.

END OF CASE 21

■ INDEPENDENT QUESTIONS

*QUESTIONS 100 to 200 do **not** refer to a case.*

100. Mr. Chelios, a 63-year-old client with type 1 diabetes, was recently diagnosed with a myocardial infarction and was started on metoprolol (Lopresor). What manifestation would require the nurse to withhold administering metoprolol?

1. Irregular heart rate
2. Significant bradycardia
3. Persistent fatigue
4. Orthostatic hypotension

101. Mr. Hansen, a 75-year-old client living in a seniors' complex, is prescribed diuretics and other medication for hypertension. What information should the nurse provide?

    1. Weigh himself at the same time each day.

    2. Have blood pressure checked twice daily.

    3. Measure and record urine output daily.

    4. Check apical pulse daily.

102. James, 12 years old, has returned to the unit following surgery. James is resting quietly and readily falls asleep. His mother states that he is a quiet boy. On assessment, James rates his pain at 7 out of 10. What should the nurse do?

    1. Continue to allow James to rest.

    2. Ask James' mother to rate her son's pain.

    3. Recognize that James has moderate-to-severe pain.

    4. Reassess James' pain using a visual analog scale.

103. The nurse is asked by a co-worker to access a family member's electronic health record for the results of a diagnostic test. What should the nurse do?

    1. Give the co-worker the access codes.

    2. Provide the information to the co-worker.

    3. Remind the co-worker that this is unprofessional behaviour.

    4. Access the health record at the end of the shift.

104. Mr. Huber, 59 years old, has a history of angina and starts experiencing chest pain while shovelling snow. His neighbour, a nurse, comes to his assistance. Mr. Huber reports that he took a nitroglycerin tablet about 5 minutes ago but that the pain has not subsided. What should the nurse do first?

    1. Check the expiry date on the prescription.

    2. Suggest that he take another nitroglycerin tablet.

    3. Transport him to the hospital.

    4. Assess his pain on a scale of 1 to 10.

105. Mr. Southworth, a 19-year-old construction worker, has been admitted to hospital following a diagnosis of type 1 diabetes. At a health-care team meeting, it is determined that Mr. Southworth is ready to begin education on self-care. What behaviour would indicate Mr. Southworth's readiness to learn?

    1. Eating all the food provided on the tray.

    2. Stating that a return to work will be impossible.

    3. Telling the nurse about a friend from work who has diabetes.

    4. Questioning the nurse about why insulin is given in different sites.

106. Devon, 13 years old, is discharged from hospital with a fractured ankle. He has a below-the-knee cast in place. What should be his discharge instructions?

    1. Insert a knitting needle into the cast to help relieve itchiness.

    2. Elevate casted extremity for 24 to 48 hours following application of cast.

    3. Take analgesics every 4 hours for the next week.

    4. Dry cast with a hair dryer if the cast should accidentally become wet.

107. The nurse is leading a planning group focusing on establishing a community kitchen for low-income and single-parent families. This is the third meeting of the group. What should the nurse do to facilitate the work of this group?

    1. Praise the strength of the individual members.

    2. Elicit individual group members' views on shared decision-making.

    3. Discuss how individual behaviour can undermine the group.

    4. Invite the group to sit around the table and eat a meal together.

108. An attending physician has requested that the nurse suture a scalp laceration. What should the nurse do?

    1. Explain the nurse's roles and responsibilities to the physician.

    2. Ask the physician to be present during the procedure.

    3. Request that the nursing educator assist with the procedure.

    4. Review the policy and procedure manual.

109. Mrs. King, 48 years old, had a myocardial infarction (MI). She is married and works in a local car plant. What information should the nurse provide?

    1. Resume sexual intercourse 5 days after an MI.

    2. Return to work 4 weeks following discharge.

    3. Walk at least 45 minutes daily.

    4. Participate in a cardiac rehabilitation program.

110. Jimmy, 12 years old, is being given an intramuscular injection by a colleague. The nurse observes the colleague landmarking for a dorsogluteal injection. What should that nurse tell the colleague?

    1. Deltoid is the preferred site in children.

    2. Ventrogluteal is the preferred site in children.

    3. Vastus lateralis is the safest site to use.

    4. Dorsogluteal site is recommended only for adults.

111. Mr. Picquot, 81 years old, recently lost his wife, son and grandson in a car accident. He has come to the clinic because he has not been sleeping. What should the nurse do?

    1. Tell him to take daily walks.

    2. Explore joining a bereavement group.

    3. Request a sedative from his physician.

    4. Refer him to a massage therapist.

112. A nurse notes that a colleague is changing her assignment to care for Mr. Bowman, her spouse's father. The other clients have reported that they are not receiving care. What should the nurse do?

    1. Speak to the nurse-in-charge.

    2. Tell the colleague not to change assignments.

    3. Report the colleague to a professional body.

    4. Speak to the colleague about her actions.

113. Mrs. Logan, 86 years old, has been transferred to a long-term care facility. The transfer notes state that Mrs. Logan is on antibiotics, is not oriented to time or place and has struck a staff member providing routine bed care. What is the first action for the admitting nurse?

    1. Assess Mrs. Logan's vital signs using a calm, non-threatening manner.

    2. Orient Mrs. Logan and explain the purpose of the admission assessment.

    3. Apply restraints prior to starting the admission assessment.

    4. Allow time for Mrs. Logan to settle into a quiet room.

114. During the evening shift, a nurse goes home sick, leaving one nurse and one practical nurse on the unit to care for 20 clients. What would indicate to the nurse that this is an unrealistic workload?

    1. Number of hours remaining in the shift

    2. Complexity of care required by the clients

    3. Administrative tasks that need completion

    4. Degree of experience of the practical nurse

115.   Mr. Raymond, 50 years old, was admitted for acute respiratory failure. He is alert but remains mechanically ventilated despite numerous attempts to wean him off the ventilator. What is the most appropriate nursing action?

1.   Remind Mr. Raymond that he needs to breathe deeper to fully expand his lungs.

2.   Advocate for Mr. Raymond to give him a day of rest on the ventilator.

3.   Ask Mr. Raymond what he believes would help him wean off the ventilator.

4.   Request an order for an anxiolytic before attempting to wean him.

116.   Mr. Sinai, 57 years old, has come to the clinic. He tells the nurse that he has not slept since learning he will lose his job in 2 weeks. What should the nurse do?

1.   Suggest that he explore other sources of employment.

2.   Discuss with him the importance of going to bed earlier.

3.   Encourage him to take a hot shower prior to bedtime.

4.   Advise him to see a lifestyle counsellor.

117.   The nurse had been providing counselling to Ms. Shetland, a 22-year-old woman with paraplegia who lives with her boyfriend. During the last home visit, the boyfriend was intoxicated and made a verbal threat to the nurse. What should the nurse do?

1.   Suggest that her boyfriend attend addictions services.

2.   Conduct the visits at the clinic.

3.   Assess for domestic violence.

4.   Visit when the boyfriend is absent.

118.   Evelyn, 7 years old, who has asthma, is admitted to hospital. She is coughing and appears restless. What does Evelyn's behaviour indicate?

1.   Manifestations of a viral infection

2.   Need for respiratory assessment

3.   Response to the warm, dry air

4.   Fatigue

119.   The nurse has developed a multimedia presentation on birth control, safe sex and pregnancy. What is the most effective strategy to promote group participation among adolescents who are familiar with each other?

1.   Organize a game between the genders about myths on the topics.

2.   Distribute a birth control kit with examples of various birth control methods.

3.   Provide handouts of the presentation content to participants.

4.   Ask the group to identify different types of birth control methods.

120. Mrs. Stone, 50 years old, has a patient-controlled analgesia (PCA) pump and she rates her pain 8 out of 10. What should the nurse do initially?

1. Administer oral pain medication immediately.
2. Contact the physician to increase the dose of the analgesia.
3. Encourage the client to push the demand button on the PCA more frequently.
4. Ask the client if she would rather receive an intramuscular injection.

121. The nurse has been assigned to a rural community health clinic to provide information to a group of pregnant teens. What should the nurse do first?

1. Determine the health-care needs of the group.
2. Establish prenatal health promotion education classes.
3. Obtain parental consent prior to the teens attending the session.
4. Conduct classes on infant care and feeding.

122. Mrs. Wakim, 51 years old, is admitted with unstable angina. Her electrocardiogram (ECG) was normal on admission. The nurse notes that she is diaphoretic and dusky in appearance and reporting some epigastric discomfort. What should the nurse do first?

1. Administer oxygen via nasal cannula.
2. Contact the ECG technician to perform an ECG.
3. Use a numeric pain scale to rate her level of pain.
4. Administer sublingual nitroglycerin.

123. While providing direct care for a 16-year-old client diagnosed with active pulmonary tuberculosis, the nurse's mask and gown become wet. What should the nurse do?

1. Remove the mask and gown and finish care quickly.
2. Continue with care of the client.
3. Change the mask and gown.
4. Ask another nurse to mask and gown and finish care.

124. Ms. Rutherford, 19 years old with a diagnosis of borderline personality disorder, has a history of engaging in self-mutilating behaviour. The nurse invites Ms. Rutherford to talk about the marks on her arm, which include both recent cuts and healed scars. What response is most consistent with the reasons given by people who engage in this behaviour?

1. "I just want to die."

2. "Everybody I know does it."

3. "The voices tell me to do it."

4. "The blood shows me I am real."

125. A 41-year-old female presents to the emergency department with a 3-hour history of centralized chest pain associated with nausea, shortness of breath and diaphoresis. What should be the nurse's initial intervention?

1. Apply oxygen and obtain a complete set of vital signs.

2. Obtain an accurate nursing history and report to the physician.

3. Encourage slow deep breaths and provide an emesis basin.

4. Provide a fan and reassure the client.

126. There has been a Norwalk virus outbreak at a small hospital that has affected 85% of the nursing staff and many clients. There is inadequate staff for the next two shifts. What should the nurse do?

1. Request that family members help with care.

2. Transfer clients to another hospital.

3. Ensure that the staff and clients use hand sanitizers.

4. Explore options for using nurses and unregulated health workers from other regions.

127. Megan, 6 years old, living with type 1 diabetes, collapses in the clinic. She is incoherent and moans when her name is called. Megan's RR is 20 and shallow and her HR is 110. The nurse is unsure of Megan's blood sugar level. What is the most appropriate intervention?

1. Three to four glucose tablets

2. Subcutaneous insulin

3. One candy

4. IM glucagon (GlucaGen)

128. What research finding should the nurse explain to a mother whose 18-year-old daughter abuses alcohol regularly?

1. It is a problem that most often affects unemployed women in their thirties.

2. Alcohol abuse results directly from the father's alcohol use.

3. A link exists between social attitudes and alcohol consumption.

4. Alcohol abuse is a sign of a personality disorder.

129. A nurse has great difficulty distancing herself from the care of a client when she leaves work. What should the nurse do?

1. Recognize that she is too compassionate.

2. Request that the client be assigned to another nurse.

3. Share her concerns with the client.

4. Confide in a colleague whom she trusts.

130. Ms. Tefry, 36 years old, is admitted with ruptured membranes and is in the early stages of labour. There is a pattern of prolonged variable decelerations on the fetal monitor tracing. In order to implement best practice, what information does the nurse need to know?

1. Variable decelerations are expected after the membranes have ruptured and labour has begun.

2. Cord compression is occurring, and fetal well-being may be compromised.

3. Variable decelerations are caused by pressure on the fetal head during contractions.

4. Uteroplacental insufficiency is occurring, and immediate steps are needed to correct it.

131. Ms. Bochuck, 44 years old, is admitted with a diagnosis of obsessive compulsive disorder. She washes her hands constantly and has a rule of washing her hands seven times after using the washroom. The nurse overhears a colleague telling the client that she may wash her hands only one time after using the washroom. What action should the nurse take?

1. Explain to the colleague that interfering with the ritual could cause Ms. Bochuck's anxiety to escalate.

2. Suggest that the colleague reassure Ms. Bochuck that there will be time to wash her hands later.

3. Encourage the colleague to explain to Ms. Bochuck that a 2-minute wash is effective.

4. Agree with the colleague that resisting handwashing will help Ms. Bochuk reduce her anxiety.

132. Mr. Simpson, 54 years old, has grandiose delusional thinking and angry outbursts. What should the nurse do?

1. Go along with the delusion to lessen his anxiety.

2. Follow a plan of care aimed at helping him explain the delusion.

3. Promote distraction to lessen his focus on the delusion.

4. Develop a plan of care aimed at changing his delusion.

133. Kassie, 18 months old, is being discharged from the pediatric unit after being diagnosed with a seizure disorder. Kassie's father asks the nurse how he can prevent Kassie from being injured during a seizure. How should the nurse respond?

1. Put an oral airway into Kassie's mouth when she has a seizure.

2. Place Kassie on her back and open her airway.

3. Gently restrain Kassie when a seizure is occurring.

4. Pad the inside of Kassie's crib rails.

134. Mrs. Stonehouse, 36 years old, has been living with chronic schizophrenia since being diagnosed 12 years ago. She has had two short hospitalizations following periods when she stopped taking her medication. She now presents at the outpatient clinic, crying and saying, "Please make them go away." What should the nurse do first?

1. Call the physician to review the medication.

2. Ask the client to describe what is happening to her.

3. Provide health teaching about adhering to her medication regime.

4. Initiate hospital admission process.

135. Which approach by the nurse facilitates continuity and consistency of a client's care?

1. Coordinate regular client-focused conferences attended by relevant health-care team members.

2. Identify the client's health-care needs on behalf of all health-care team members.

3. Communicate individually with each health-care team member.

4. Make decisions regarding the client's care on the basis of input from all health-care team members.

136. What action would best allow the nurse to provide culturally competent care?

1. Learning about different cultures

2. Learning key phrases in other languages

3. Recognizing biases and personal assumptions

4. Travelling to become familiar with other cultures

137. Mrs. Norton, 87 years old, is concerned about contracting *Clostridium difficile*. What should the nurse suggest?

1. Limit the use of antibiotics.

2. Follow a balanced diet.

3. Avoid contact with infected persons.

4. Practise good handwashing throughout the day.

138. The community health nurse is giving a presentation to a parenting group. What action would provide the nurse with initial feedback on the nurse's teaching skills?

    1. Elicit the group's feelings about the presentation.

    2. Observe the group's non-verbal behaviour.

    3. Ask the group to complete a feedback questionnaire.

    4. Administer a quiz on the content of the presentation.

139. The nurse is preparing to administer an angiotensin receptor blocker. What is the best description of the effect of this category of drugs?

    1. Vasodilation; decreases blood pressure

    2. Vasodilation; no effect on blood pressure

    3. Vasoconstriction; decreases blood pressure

    4. Vasoconstriction; no effect on blood pressure

140. Lydia, 14 years old, has been diagnosed with anorexia nervosa. In the first counselling session, the nurse establishes a positive rapport with the client. What should the nurse do in the second session?

    1. Explain that her illness is a result of communication problems within her family.

    2. Make a contract with her for food and fluid intake to restore health.

    3. Inform her that it is important to follow a diet provided by a nutritionist.

    4. Advise Lydia that she should avoid power struggles with authority figures.

141. Jon, 15 years old, asks the community health nurse what is the greatest health risk for his age group. How should the nurse respond?

    1. Suicide

    2. Substance abuse

    3. Eating disorders

    4. Unintentional injuries

142. Mrs. Jacobsen, 62 years old, is diagnosed with heart failure and atrial fibrillation. She is taking warfarin sodium (Coumadin). She tells the nurse that she is taking several herbs to improve her energy level. How should the nurse respond?

    1. Support the client in her choice to use complementary medicine.

    2. Ask the client to identify the herbs that she is using.

    3. Inform the client that herbs are contraindicated while taking warfarin sodium.

    4. Advise the client that there is no evidence that herbs improve fatigue.

143. Mr. Dionne, 87 years old, has recently had a stroke (brain attack) and is unable to mobilize independently. What assessment tool would most accurately predict this client's risk for skin breakdown?

1. Glasgow coma scale

2. Neurovascular profile

3. Braden scale

4. CAGE questionnaire

144. How should the nurse evaluate the effectiveness of health teaching with Tyler, 5 years old, who is living with cystic fibrosis?

1. Watch him prepare his medications.

2. Tell him to describe to his mother what cystic fibrosis is.

3. Ask him if he understands everything that has been taught.

4. Ask him to point out different areas for chest physiotherapy on a doll.

145. Juan, 18 years old, has been treated for positive symptoms of schizophrenia. He tells the nurse, "I want to go home to Neptune but the responder in my ear is broken. My family will never find me. There is nobody like me here." What is the best nursing response?

1. "Nobody can live on Neptune. Tell me where you really live."

2. "It sounds like you are feeling really lonely."

3. "Almost everyone here is around your age. I can introduce you to some new friends."

4. "The people on Neptune likely have responders that can find you anywhere."

146. The nurse is assigned two male clients with the same last name. What action can the nurse take to ensure client safety?

1. Transfer one of the clients to another unit.

2. Make a note on the medication record.

3. Ask a co-worker to care for one of the clients.

4. Ensure that the clients are in separate rooms.

147. The nurse on a busy surgical unit is asked by a student nurse to explain a client's diagnosis. How should the nurse respond to the student's request?

1. Direct the student to the instructor.

2. Show the student where the textbooks are stored.

3. Tell the student that she does not have time.

4. Ask the student to join her during a break.

148. Which action is appropriate for a nurse transcribing medication orders?

    1. Record oral route when the route is not specified.

    2. Ensure trailing zeros are written with drug orders (e.g., 1.0 mg).

    3. Ask a colleague to decipher illegible orders.

    4. Establish if the client has allergies to the drug.

149. What is a reason for polypharmacy in older adults?

    1. There is no predictable pattern in the metabolism of medications.

    2. Tolerance to medications has developed over time.

    3. Many specialists are prescribing medications filled at multiple pharmacies.

    4. Older adults tend to share medications with each other.

150. Mr. Prakash, 67 years old, is in acute renal failure. What should the nurse do initially?

    1. Monitor for hypokalemia.

    2. Encourage ambulation.

    3. Auscultate for breath sounds.

    4. Assess for dehydration.

151. The nurse is teaching a prenatal class to a group of women about pain relief measures during labour. A young woman states, "I prefer not to use any medication during labour; aromatherapy oils have a calming effect on me." What is the nurse's most appropriate response?

    1. Aromatherapy oils may work for mild pain but will not reduce labour pain.

    2. Alternatives should be considered because aromatherapy may not be sufficient to manage labour pain.

    3. Aromatherapy oils are a good choice to use with medication for labour pain.

    4. Checks need to be made to ensure that the aromatherapy oils are safe to use during labour.

152. A client is prescribed furosemide (Lasix) 20 mg p.o. b.i.d. at 08:00 and 14:00. After administering the 08:00 medication, the nurse realizes that furosemide 40 mg was administered in error. What should the nurse do?

    1. Note the error in the nursing notes.

    2. Withhold the 14:00 dose of furosemide.

    3. Submit an incident report to the unit manager.

    4. Notify the pharmacist of the error.

153. At the start of the shift, Fred, a nurse, introduces himself to a client and tells him he will be his nurse. The client states that another staff member has already indicated that she is going to be the nurse. What should Fred do?

 1. Apologize to the client for the mistake.

 2. Clarify his role to the client.

 3. Indicate that there will be more than one nurse.

 4. Ask for a description of the nurse.

154. Mrs. Jones, 45 years old, presents to the emergency department with chest pain. She is anxious, restless and apprehensive. What should the nurse do?

 1. Inform Mrs. Jones that it is normal to feel anxious in the emergency department.

 2. Stay with Mrs. Jones and provide emotional support.

 3. Remain close to Mrs. Jones when delivering care to other clients.

 4. Explain the purpose of the various monitoring devices in the emergency department.

155. Mrs. Ross, 35 years old, returns to the nursing unit following major abdominal surgery. One hour later, Mrs. Ross is drowsy and nauseated, her RR is 14, HR 70, BP 98/60 and pain is 3 out of 10. Which prescribed medication should the nurse administer?

 1. Morphine sulfate (Morphine)

 2. Dimenhydrinate (Gravol)

 3. Naloxone (Narcan)

 4. Lorazcpam (Ativan)

156. The nurse has completed a research study and found that many of the clients in the geriatric clinic do not complete regular breast self-examinations. What should the nurse do to initiate a change in practice?

 1. Develop a new policy for the clinic on breast self-examination.

 2. Create a questionnaire asking clients to identify barriers to breast self-examination.

 3. Present the research to the health-care team.

 4. Consult with the geriatric nurse educator.

157. What should the nurse recommend to a prenatal class to reduce the risk of sudden infant death syndrome?

 1. Place an electronic air filter in the infant's room.

 2. Wrap the infant in a warm blanket.

 3. Place the infant in the supine position for sleeping.

 4. Place an infant monitor in the baby's room.

158. What is the appropriate nursing action when the air in a client's room smells of marijuana and the client appears to be euphoric?

    1. Call the client's family for further information.

    2. File a written report with the security department.

    3. Report the incident immediately to the physician.

    4. Document on the care plan to observe for illicit drug use.

159. The nurse asks a physician for clarification of an order. The physician yells at the nurse and tells the nurse to learn to read it. What should the nurse do?

    1. Ask a co-worker to clarify the order.

    2. Apologize to the physician.

    3. File a complaint with the medical association.

    4. Report the incident to the nurse-in-charge.

160. Mr. Davies, 62 years old, has significant anemia and consents to receiving a blood transfusion. Shortly after the transfusion is initiated, he calls the nurse and states that he does not think having a blood transfusion is a good idea and that his heart is racing. He is anxious, has a red face and is breathing rapidly. What is the most appropriate action?

    1. Explore the reasons why Mr. Davies is anxious about receiving a blood transfusion.

    2. Explain in a calm manner why a blood transfusion is recommended for anemia.

    3. Document that the blood transfusion has been discontinued at the client's request.

    4. Stop the blood transfusion and take the client's vital signs.

161. Mrs. Pike, 90 years old, has a 3-day history of nausea and vomiting. Her mucous membranes are dry, and she has poor skin turgor. The physician orders an IV infusion of a litre bag of normal saline over 10 hours. What should the nurse do first?

    1. Insert an IV and connect to a litre bag of normal saline and infuse at a rate of 100 mL/h.

    2. Explain the procedure and the reason for the IV infusion to the client.

    3. Encourage fluids and then start the IV infusion.

    4. Insert an IV in an area that does not interfere with the client's activities of daily living.

162. The nurse is teaching a group of older adults at a wellness clinic. What is the primary rationale for beginning each teaching session with 5 minutes of warm-up exercise?

1. To improve circulation

2. To promote social interaction

3. To decrease immobility

4. To promote good sleep habits

163. Mrs. Nissan, 82 years old, is being cared for by home support workers. Her daughter is considering admitting her to a long-term care facility. Mrs. Nissan has methicillin-resistant *Staphylococcus aureus* (MRSA). What information should the nurse provide?

1. Studies show that home care is healthier for persons with resistance to antibiotics.

2. Hospitalization will ensure that Mrs. Nissan receives interprofessional care.

3. Family members should receive yearly vaccines to prevent the spread of MRSA.

4. Frequent changes in home support persons are essential when the client has MRSA.

164. A physician has ordered a dry dressing to be applied to an open leg ulcer. The nurse is aware that this is no longer current best practice. What should the nurse do first?

1. Complete the dressing change as ordered.

2. Inform the physician that this is not best practice.

3. Use the best practice method for the dressing change.

4. Ask the manager to develop a policy regarding appropriate dressings.

165. Mr. Smithers, 71 years old, weighs 115 kg and has obstructive sleep apnea (OSA). Mr. Smithers is reluctant to wear his continuous positive airway pressure (CPAP) therapy apparatus. What information should the nurse provide?

1. Weight loss will cure sleep apnea.

2. The severity of OSA increases with age.

3. The need for CPAP therapy will decrease with dedicated use.

4. Relaxation of the throat muscles causes obstruction in OSA.

166. The public health department has announced an avian flu pandemic. What information should the nurse provide to the public?

1. Annual flu immunization will offer protection.

2. People must obtain antiviral medication.

3. Schools will be closed.

4. Health-care personnel will come from other communities.

167. The nurse is visiting older adults who are living in a personal care home. The nurse observes the older adults bumping into chairs placed near entrances to the common rooms and front door. What should the nurse do first?

1. Organize a meeting with the older adults who are having difficulty.

2. Discuss observations with the manager of the home.

3. Assist the older adults to move the chairs to another area.

4. Suggest that the older adults have their vision checked as soon as possible.

168. What is the best way for the nurse manager to integrate a large group of newly graduated nurses into a unit?

1. Draw names to pair each new staff member with a senior nurse.

2. Ask the nurse educator to mentor the new staff.

3. Have regular meetings with the group.

4. Encourage weekly presentations shared by senior and new staff.

169. The nurse is researching data about pain management on the Internet. What criterion indicates that a health-related Internet site is reliable?

1. Author's name is stated.

2. Site is sponsored by a pharmaceutical company.

3. Frequency of updates is given.

4. User testimonials are provided.

170. What are some of the most common causes of cystitis?

1. Indwelling catheters, urologic instrumentation and sexual intercourse

2. Sexually transmitted infection, abnormal Pap test and vaginal discharge

3. Stress incontinence, urge incontinence and total incontinence

4. Type 2 diabetes, pregnancy and gout

171. Mr. Clark, 54 years old, is receiving intravenous antibiotics for cellulitis. Ten minutes after the infusion is completed, he reports feeling anxious and nauseated. His face is flushed and he is diaphoretic. What should the nurse do first?

   1. Withhold the next dose.

   2. Request an order to treat the side effects.

   3. Report and document.

   4. Apply oxygen by nasal cannula.

172. Mr. Ferris, 24 years old, arrives at the emergency department with abdominal pain. The physician orders an analgesic. A colleague states that a placebo has previously worked to alleviate Mr. Ferris' pain. What is the nurse's best response to the colleague?

   1. A positive attitude can eliminate pain.

   2. The placebo will bind to opioid receptors to reduce pain.

   3. The client may not have been in pain previously.

   4. Placebo administration may affect the trust relationship.

173. The nurse is working with a group of older adults and health-care professionals to plan an educational day on emotional health in later life. What should the team consider while planning the event?

   1. Emotional health in older adults is difficult to determine.

   2. Mental health services for older adults are well developed.

   3. Anxiety disorders rarely occur in older adults.

   4. Suicide is a significant problem among older women.

174. Ms. Rallyea, 58 years old, is admitted with severe clinical depression and is started on antidepressant medications. Her mood has remained low and she has not initiated conversation. On the 15th day of hospitalization, she informs the nurse that she is feeling great and energetic. What should the nurse do?

   1. Notify the social worker of the improvement to schedule a discharge planning conference.

   2. Invite Ms. Rallyea to talk and ask her if she is thinking of hurting herself.

   3. Report to the team that the antidepressant medication is effective.

   4. Chart the mood change and share the observation at the team meeting the next day.

175. What finding would indicate that a nasogastric tube is functioning ineffectively?

    1. Nausea and abdominal bloating

    2. Hypoactive bowel sounds

    3. Sore throat and reflux

    4. Intermittent brown drainage

176. Mrs. Jenkins, 25 years old, had a cesarian section 30 minutes ago and is now in the recovery room. What is the earliest sign of complication?

    1. Bloody staining on the abdominal dressing

    2. Scant or no lochial flow on the perineal pad

    3. Hematuria and a systolic BP above 100 mmHg

    4. Fundal height is three-finger widths above the umbilicus

177. Mrs. Osbourne, 92 years old, is in a long-term care facility for respite while her daughter, the primary caregiver, is on vacation. A recent chest X-ray indicates that Mrs. Osborne has pulmonary tuberculosis. Which nursing action is most appropriate?

    1. Administer antibiotics to Mrs. Osbourne while she is in the facility.

    2. Notify the daughter of her mother's diagnosis.

    3. Obtain a list of people who had contact with Mrs. Osbourne in the past 2 weeks.

    4. Ask the infection control nurse to administer a tuberculin skin test to staff.

178. Mr. Bachant, 68 years old, is brought to the emergency department following a motor vehicle collision. Upon presentation, he is pale and anxious and reports posterior neck pain. He has an obvious deformity to his right forearm. What should be the nurse's initial intervention?

    1. Check circulation, colour and range of motion of right forearm.

    2. Check vital signs and provide comfort to the client.

    3. Apply a hard cervical collar and check neurovascular signs.

    4. Apply a splint to the right forearm and elevate the extremity.

179. Ms. Jones, 33 years old, is admitted for labour induction. Ms. Jones questions the need for the fetal monitor. How should the nurse respond?

    1. Tell Ms. Jones not to worry since the fetal monitor will not harm her or the baby.

    2. Discuss with Ms. Jones that fetal monitoring is hospital policy.

    3. Inform Ms. Jones that the fetal monitoring allows nurses to see how the baby is coping with labour contractions.

    4. Explain to Ms. Jones that fetal monitoring provides a warning to prepare for a cesarian section if required.

180. A 57-year-old male client had abdominal surgery 5 days ago. Shortly after the staples are removed, the client reports a "release of pressure" after a period of coughing. The nurse's assessment reveals moderate serosanguineous oozing and slightly separated wound edges. What should be the nurse's priority action?

1. Prepare the client for immediate surgery.

2. Cleanse the wound with saline and apply dressing.

3. Teach the client proper splinting with position changes.

4. Apply a pressure dressing immediately.

181. A biophysical profile (BPP) is a common diagnostic tool used for the antepartum client. What information is commonly obtained with this tool?

1. Presence of fetal fine motor movement

2. Colour and amount of the amniotic fluid

3. Weight and length of the fetus

4. Fetal heart rate patterns

182. Mrs. Raymond, 90 years old, is in a long-term care facility. Her family is pleased with the nursing care that she has received from a nurse in the facility. Her family invites the nurse to dinner at their home. What is the nurse's most appropriate response?

1. "Even though I care about Mrs. Raymond, it is not appropriate for me to accept."

2. "I cannot come to your home. Would it be possible to meet at a restaurant?"

3. "I would love to come, but I will have to check with my supervisor first."

4. "Thank you very much. What day would you like me to come?"

183. Brooke is a 2-day old, full-term newborn who was delivered following a prolonged labour. She is breastfeeding poorly today. Vital signs are T 35.8-37.7 °C, HR 102, RR 38. She is irritable and jaundiced and has some petechiae on her trunk and legs. What should the nurse conclude from these findings?

1. The physician needs to be contacted immediately because Brooke may have an advanced systemic infection.

2. Brooke is adapting normally but needs to be kept warmer to improve signs of cold stress and hypoglycemia.

3. These physical responses are a result of ineffective breastfeeding and hyperbilirubinemia.

4. These are all signs of hypoglycemia and Brooke needs to have both blood glucose and bilirubin levels evaluated.

184. The nurse is developing a health promotion program for a group of older adults. What is the most effective way to develop this program?

1. Discuss their ability to access health care.

2. Identify their definitions of health in a focus group.

3. Assist in identifying their health risk factors.

4. Circulate a health questionnaire.

185. Johnny, 6 months old, has a gastrostomy tube for feeding in place. What would indicate to the home care nurse that Johnny's mother is ready to learn to care for her son?

1. Reading the pamphlets the nurse provided

2. Requesting to attend a support group

3. Asking the nurse to develop a plan of care

4. Stating that flushing tubes appears easy

186. Mr. Godfrey, 24 years old, has been treated for schizophrenia since he was 18 years old. He lives at home with his parents. His parents report that he spends his days sleeping or watching television, shows little facial expression, rarely talks and never seems to enjoy anything. How should the nurse respond?

1. The behaviours described are typical negative symptoms of schizophrenia.

2. Mr. Godfrey is demonstrating behaviour related to shame at not being able to live independently.

3. The dose of the antipsychotic medication is too high and is causing sedation.

4. Mr. Godfrey is likely experiencing depression as well as schizophrenia.

187. An outreach team is formed to work with homeless people in a community. Utilizing the principles of primary health care, what is an appropriate intervention for the team?

1. Provide services that are aimed at disease prevention.

2. Focus on services that fall within the health-care system.

3. Manage health-care needs for the individuals.

4. Work with other community groups to improve services.

188. On the basis of a community needs assessment, the public health nurse develops a program to prevent childhood obesity. What strategy is most appropriate for successful implementation?

1. Provide information to the teacher for classroom use.

2. Involve parents, teachers and children in program development.

3. Ask the school administration to remove all vending machines.

4. Initiate an exercise program for obese children during recess.

189. Mrs. Greer, 25 years old, has undergone an emergency cesarian section. She is experiencing severe pain after the procedure and does not want to hold her baby. What should the nurse do?

    1. Advise Mrs. Greer that holding her baby will help distract her from the pain.

    2. Explain to Mrs. Greer the importance of bonding with the baby.

    3. Inform Mrs. Greer that pain is to be expected and give her a warm blanket.

    4. Administer analgesia and reassess Mrs. Greer's comfort level.

190. While caring for a client, a nurse notices a colleague giving a baby his dose of digoxin (Lanoxin) without taking the baby's apical pulse. The nurse is aware that the colleague has been reprimanded by the nursing supervisor about unsafe practice. What would be the most appropriate action for the nurse to take?

    1. Report the incident to the physician.

    2. Report the incident to the nurse-in-charge.

    3. Talk to the nurse colleague privately about what was observed.

    4. Take the baby's pulse after the colleague leaves the room.

191. Mr. Stone, 64 years old, suddenly develops chest pain radiating to his left arm 5 days following a myocardial infarction. What should the nurse do first?

    1. Check the client's blood pressure and administer sublingual nitroglycerin.

    2. Assess the client's level of pain and administer acetaminophen (Tylenol).

    3. Reassure the client that this pain is common following a myocardial infarction.

    4. Obtain an electrocardiogram and report the pain to the physician.

192. Mrs. Singh, 76 years old, had a total abdominal hysterectomy 48 hours ago. Meperidine (Demerol) 50-75 mg IM is ordered q.4-6h p.r.n. for pain. Meperidine 50 mg IM has been administered approximately every 5 hours since she returned from surgery. Mrs. Singh reports that the meperidine is working "quite well" but the nurse observes that Mrs. Singh is becoming tremulous and slightly agitated. What is the most appropriate nursing intervention?

    1. Administer a higher dosage of meperidine to reduce agitation related to pain.

    2. Contact the physician to request an order for naloxone (Narcan).

    3. Administer lorazepam (Ativan) for anxiety related to her surgery.

    4. Contact the physician to request an alternative analgesic order.

193. Cody, 3 years old, is admitted with acute asthma. What would indicate that Cody is in advanced respiratory failure?

    1. Bradycardia

    2. Tachycardia

    3. Restlessness

    4. Nasal flaring

194. What intervention best facilitates successful stress management with clients?

    1. Teaching relaxation techniques

    2. Suggesting talking with others

    3. Encouraging problem-solving

    4. Promoting self-awareness

195. Marisa, 5 years old, is being discharged home. Her parents both smoke cigarettes. What information should the nurse share about second-hand smoke?

    1. Blowing smoke outside a window will make smoking indoors safer.

    2. Inhaling second-hand smoke is more dangerous than smoking a cigarette.

    3. Establish a designated smoking room that the child will not have access to.

    4. Ensure that the windows are down if smoking in the car.

196. Mr. Janes, 50 years old, presents to the emergency department with a 2-hour history of chest pain associated with shortness of breath. During the nurse's assessment, Mr. Janes suddenly collapses on the stretcher. What should be the nurse's priority action?

    1. Open airway with the head-chin-tilt lift manoeuvre.

    2. Check for the carotid pulse.

    3. Determine responsiveness.

    4. Perform tongue-jaw lift to see if a foreign body is visible.

197. What is the most appropriate strategy for teaching kindergarten children effective handwashing techniques?

    1. Explaining and demonstrating the proper procedure for handwashing

    2. Involving the children in imitative and imaginative techniques on handwashing

    3. Developing a poster showing colourful bacteria growing on hands

    4. Providing a video for the children to watch at home

198.	At the beginning of an educational session that includes a video on prostate cancer, the nurse finds the group of men, 65 to 75 years, apprehensive and embarrassed to discuss the topic. Considering the group's behaviour, how should the nurse approach this situation?

　　1.	Acknowledge the group's discomfort with the topic.

　　2.	Reduce the apprehension by telling an amusing anecdote.

　　3.	Recognize that this is a common response in this age group and begin the session.

　　4.	Give the group time to ease into the topic by starting the session with the video.

199.	Mrs. Lee, 62 years old with chronic arthritis pain, tells the community health nurse that she has cut back on her prescribed medication because she started taking glucosamine. Mrs. Lee has lost 5 kg in the past month and she states that it is getting harder to prepare meals. What action should the nurse take?

　　1.	Inform the client that glucosamine is not a proven treatment.

　　2.	Teach the client how poor nutrition will complicate her condition.

　　3.	Explain the action of the prescribed medication to the client.

　　4.	Schedule an appointment for Mrs. Lee to see her physician.

200.	Mrs. Dicker, 70 years old, has terminal cancer and is being cared for by her husband. Mr. Dicker remarks that it upsets him to see his wife drink so little. He asks if there is anything that can be done because he does not want her to die of thirst. What action would best address his concerns?

　　1.	Contact the physician for an order to initiate an IV.

　　2.	Arrange to admit Mrs. Dicker to the hospital for rehydration.

　　3.	Call the family physician for an order to insert a nasogastric tube.

　　4.	Encourage Mr. Dicker to keep his wife's lips moist and have fluids available.

END OF INDEPENDENT QUESTIONS

END OF THE BOOK

CHAPTER 5:
CALCULATING YOUR SCORE

■ CALCULATING YOUR SCORE

The following steps can be used to calculate your total score on the practice questions.

1. Locate the answer key at the end of this chapter.

2. Tally up your responses that correspond to the correct answers indicated on the answer key. (Mark the questions you answered incorrectly by circling or highlighting them on your answer sheet or by listing them on a separate sheet of paper. This will make it easier for you to create your performance profile, explained in chapter 6.)

3. Score one point for each correct answer. Incorrect or blank responses receive a score of zero. Be sure to review your answer sheet for "double responses" to questions (i.e., where you selected more than one answer to a single question). Double responses are scored as zero, even if one of the answers selected is correct.

4. Use the chart below to record your total raw score.

Number of questions answered correctly

Total raw score . . . . _____ /200

You can use the following formula to convert your total raw score into a percentage.

$$\frac{\text{Total raw score}}{200} \times 100 = \underline{\hspace{2cm}} \%$$

■ INTERPRETING YOUR SCORE

The raw score and percentage score that you calculate can provide useful feedback on your performance. By using the score interpretation scale on page 84, you can obtain a quick assessment of your performance on the practice questions along with some follow-up steps you should take to enhance your preparation for the CRNE. Note that no specific pass mark is set for the practice questions.

■ HOW THE CRNE IS SCORED

The scoring of the CRNE is carried out under the direction of CNA. The multiple-choice questions are computer-scored. Only answers recorded on your answer sheet are scanned and scored. You will not receive any credit for questions that are answered in the test booklet but not on the answer sheet. Likewise, no credit will be given where you selected more than one answer to a single question.

Once the questions are marked, your score on the exam is calculated and your "pass" or "fail" result is determined by comparing this score to the established standard (pass mark).

The standard to be met on the CRNE is set in reference to the content and the level of difficulty of the questions on the exam. The standard-setting procedure involves convening a panel of subject matter experts (the examination committee), representing each provincial and territorial jurisdiction that uses the CRNE. This examination committee rates the CRNE questions on the basis of the expected performance of an entry-level registered nurse.

In the process of rating the questions, the examination committee also considers a variety of relevant criteria to ensure that the standard that candidates will be required to achieve on the CRNE is valid and fair. These criteria may include information on the preparation of new graduates, data on the performance of candidates on previous administrations of the CRNE and pertinent research findings.

On the basis of all this information, a point is set on a measurement scale that represents the required standard. The standard is set as a specific score necessary to pass that particular version of the CRNE. This standard, once established, is then approved by CNA.

Regardless of the version of the exam that is administered, a candidate's score is converted to a common measurement scale and compared against the established passing point on that scale. Although different forms of the exam contain different sets of questions, this conversion ensures that all candidates are treated fairly and are evaluated against the same standard. If your score on this common scale is at or higher than the passing point, you will receive a "pass" result on the exam, and if your score is lower than the passing point, you will receive a "fail" result on the exam.

Your pass/fail result on the CRNE is reported on the *Report Card* that is sent to you by your regulatory authority. Candidates who do not pass the CRNE are provided with additional feedback on their test performance. This feedback is similar to the information you will obtain by creating your performance profile (see chapter 6).

SCORE INTERPRETATION SCALE

RAW SCORE	PERFORMANCE	SUGGESTIONS FOR FOLLOW-UP
	STRONG	Review the rationales for the questions you answered incorrectly. The closer your score is to the borderline zone, the more you should consult the relevant texts that are cited. As well, by creating your performance profile (see chapter 6), you may identify specific areas on which you should focus during your remaining preparation time. Revisit the competencies in Appendix A for any areas you were weak in. Before writing the CRNE, take another look at the practice questions that you answered incorrectly.
	BORDERLINE	Create your performance profile to determine your areas of strength and weakness, and follow the strategies provided for dealing with your identified weaknesses (see chapter 6). Review some general nursing textbooks and some specific nursing textbooks concentrating on the problem areas. Also, review the content related to the competencies in the areas where you need improvement (see Appendix A). After your review, retake the practice questions before writing the CRNE.
	WEAK	Create your performance profile (see chapter 6) to gain a better understanding of your areas of weakness in the competency categories. In addition to reviewing some key nursing textbooks, be sure to read the rationales for all the questions. You may also benefit from reviewing the test-taking strategies (see chapter 3). Finally, retake the practice questions before writing the CRNE.

You may also benefit from assessing your readiness to write the CRNE by taking the CRNE Readiness Test (see chapter 8), available for purchase through CNA's website, www.cna-aiic.ca, or by going directly to http://readiness.cna-aiic.ca/.

ANSWER KEY FOR PREP GUIDE EXAMINATION

1.	Answer: 2	27.	Answer: 2	53.	Answer: 2	79.	Answer: 3
2.	Answer: 1	28.	Answer: 2	54.	Answer: 1	80.	Answer: 2
3.	Answer: 2	29.	Answer: 3	55.	Answer: 3	81.	Answer: 2
4.	Answer: 4	30.	Answer: 4	56.	Answer: 2	82.	Answer: 1
5.	Answer: 1	31.	Answer: 1	57.	Answer: 3	83.	Answer: 3
6.	Answer: 3	32.	Answer: 2	58.	Answer: 3	84.	Answer: 2
7.	Answer: 2	33.	Answer: 3	59.	Answer: 3	85.	Answer: 2
8.	Answer: 3	34.	Answer: 2	60.	Answer: 2	86.	Answer: 2
9.	Answer: 3	35.	Answer: 3	61.	Answer: 1	87.	Answer: 2
10.	Answer: 2	36.	Answer: 4	62.	Answer: 1	88.	Answer: 1
11.	Answer: 2	37.	Answer: 3	63.	Answer: 1	89.	Answer: 1
12.	Answer: 1	38.	Answer: 2	64.	Answer: 3	90.	Answer: 1
13.	Answer: 4	39.	Answer: 3	65.	Answer: 4	91.	Answer: 4
14.	Answer: 2	40.	Answer: 4	66.	Answer: 1	92.	Answer: 1
15.	Answer: 1	41.	Answer: 3	67.	Answer: 4	93.	Answer: 2
16.	Answer: 4	42.	Answer: 4	68.	Answer: 1	94.	Answer: 2
17.	Answer: 1	43.	Answer: 3	69.	Answer: 3	95.	Answer: 2
18.	Answer: 1	44.	Answer: 2	70.	Answer: 3	96.	Answer: 3
19.	Answer: 3	45.	Answer: 4	71.	Answer: 2	97.	Answer: 1
20.	Answer: 1	46.	Answer: 1	72.	Answer: 4	98.	Answer: 4
21.	Answer: 2	47.	Answer: 2	73.	Answer: 4	99.	Answer: 1
22.	Answer: 4	48.	Answer: 3	74.	Answer: 3	100.	Answer: 2
23.	Answer: 1	49.	Answer: 4	75.	Answer: 2	101.	Answer: 1
24.	Answer: 3	50.	Answer: 2	76.	Answer: 1	102.	Answer: 3
25.	Answer: 3	51.	Answer: 1	77.	Answer: 3	103.	Answer: 3
26.	Answer: 1	52.	Answer: 3	78.	Answer: 3	104.	Answer: 2

105. Answer: 4	133. Answer: 4	161. Answer: 2	189. Answer: 4
106. Answer: 2	134. Answer: 2	162. Answer: 1	190. Answer: 2
107. Answer: 3	135. Answer: 1	163. Answer: 1	191. Answer: 1
108. Answer: 1	136. Answer: 3	164. Answer: 2	192. Answer: 4
109. Answer: 4	137. Answer: 4	165. Answer: 4	193. Answer: 1
110. Answer: 2	138. Answer: 2	166. Answer: 3	194. Answer: 4
111. Answer: 2	139. Answer: 1	167. Answer: 2	195. Answer: 2
112. Answer: 4	140. Answer: 2	168. Answer: 4	196. Answer: 3
113. Answer: 4	141. Answer: 4	169. Answer: 3	197. Answer: 2
114. Answer: 2	142. Answer: 2	170. Answer: 1	198. Answer: 1
115. Answer: 3	143. Answer: 3	171. Answer: 3	199. Answer: 3
116. Answer: 3	144. Answer: 4	172. Answer: 4	200. Answer: 4
117. Answer: 3	145. Answer: 2	173. Answer: 1	
118. Answer: 2	146. Answer: 2	174. Answer: 2	
119. Answer: 1	147. Answer: 4	175. Answer: 1	
120. Answer: 3	148. Answer: 4	176. Answer: 4	
121. Answer: 1	149. Answer: 3	177. Answer: 2	
122. Answer: 1	150. Answer: 3	178. Answer: 3	
123. Answer: 3	151. Answer: 4	179. Answer: 3	
124. Answer: 4	152. Answer: 3	180. Answer: 2	
125. Answer: 1	153. Answer: 2	181. Answer: 4	
126. Answer: 4	154. Answer: 2	182. Answer: 1	
127. Answer: 4	155. Answer: 2	183. Answer: 1	
128. Answer: 3	156. Answer: 1	184. Answer: 2	
129. Answer: 4	157. Answer: 3	185. Answer: 1	
130. Answer: 2	158. Answer: 4	186. Answer: 1	
131. Answer: 1	159. Answer: 4	187. Answer: 4	
132. Answer: 3	160. Answer: 4	188. Answer: 2	

CHAPTER 6:
CREATING YOUR PERFORMANCE PROFILE

■ CREATING YOUR PERFORMANCE PROFILE

Once you have completed and scored the practice questions, you can create a personalized performance profile that allows you to identify your areas of strength and weakness on the practice test. You will need your scored answer sheets (or a list of the questions you answered incorrectly), the performance profile tally sheet and performance profile chart (found in the Additional Materials section at the end of the prep guide) and a calculator. If you complete your practice questions using the CD-ROM, your performance profile is automatically generated.

CLASSIFICATION OF QUESTIONS

The prep guide questions are designed to mirror actual CRNE questions as closely as possible. As a result, the structure and appearance of the questions for the prep guide are chosen on the basis of the same classification scheme that governs the CRNE. The classification schemes are:

- Competency Framework (Professional Practice, Nurse-Client Partnership, Health and Wellness, Changes in Health)

- Taxonomy Levels of Cognitive Ability (Knowledge/ Comprehension, Application, Critical Thinking)

These classifications are weighted on the basis of the *Blueprint for the Canadian Registered Nurse Examination June 2010 - May 2015*. The weights are shown as a percentage range, which stipulates the percentage of questions from each classification that are on the CRNE. For a detailed explanation of the classifications, see chapter 2.

Understanding the percentage breakdown of the variables will help you decide where to focus your study. In chapter 7, you can find each question's classifications beside the question's rationale.

STEPS FOR CREATING YOUR PERFORMANCE PROFILE

Step 1 – In chapter 5, you scored the practice questions and identified the questions you answered incorrectly. For each question you answered incorrectly, place an "X" in the rationale section beside the corresponding classifications (see chapter 7).

Step 2 – The performance profile tally sheet and the performance profile chart are located in the Additional Materials section at the back of the prep guide and can be easily removed. Three tables associated with each classification enable you to tally your scores from your multiple attempts at the practice questions. Using multiple tables also enables you to compare multiple writings to see how you are progressing.

Sample – Step 2 illustrates how to complete the tables in your performance profile tally sheet. For each question you answered incorrectly, place a mark in the row that corresponds to the competency category for that question. Do the same for the taxonomy of cognitive ability levels.

SAMPLE – STEP 2 PERFORMANCE PROFILE TALLY

Table 1: Competency Category

CATEGORY		TOTAL INCORRECT		TOTAL IN CATEGORIES		% INCORRECT	
Professional Practice ＬＨＴ l			÷	34	x	100 =	%
Nurse-Client Partnership ＬＨＴ ＬＨＴ			÷	23	x	100 =	%
Health and Wellness ＬＨＴ llll			÷	47	x	100 =	%
Changes in Health ＬＨＴ ＬＨＴ ll			÷	96	x	100 =	%
Total Incorrect			÷	**200**	**x**	**100 =**	%

Step 3 – Total the marks in the rows to determine the number of questions you answered incorrectly in each category.

Step 4 – Calculate the percentage of questions you answered incorrectly for each category. To calculate the percentage, divide the number of questions you answered incorrectly by the total number of questions for that category and multiply by 100 (See Sample – Steps 3 and 4). Repeat this for the taxonomy of cognitive ability levels.

SAMPLE – STEPS 3 AND 4 PERFORMANCE PROFILE TALLY

CATEGORY		TOTAL INCORRECT		TOTAL IN CATEGORIES		% INCORRECT	
Professional Practice ＬＨＴ l		6	÷	34	x	100 =	18 %
Nurse-Client Partnership ＬＨＴ ＬＨＴ		10	÷	23	x	100 =	43 %
Health and Wellness ＬＨＴ llll		9	÷	47	x	100 =	19 %
Changes in Health ＬＨＴ ＬＨＴ ll		12	÷	96	x	100 =	13 %
Total Incorrect		37	÷	**200**	**x**	**100 =**	18.5 %

Step 5 – Create your performance profile by taking the percentage values from each category and darkening the corresponding rows on the performance profile chart (see Sample – Step 5).

SAMPLE – STEP 5 PERFORMANCE PROFILE CHART

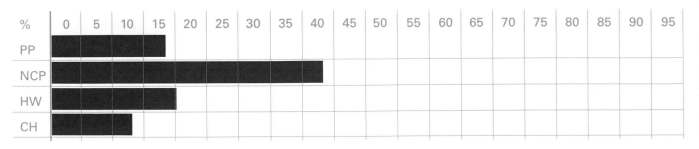

INTERPRETING YOUR PERFORMANCE

The goal in creating your performance profile is to identify your areas of relative strength and weakness. This information can help you make the best use of your remaining preparation time.

COMPETENCY CATEGORY RESULTS

Generally, those categories in which you obtained a high percentage of incorrect answers are the areas you should focus on during your remaining preparation time. However, this approach can be further refined to arrive at a more accurate diagnosis.

In looking at each table on the tally sheets, you will notice that the total number of questions in each category (i.e., the number by which you must divide) varies; some areas have relatively few questions whereas other areas have many. This is an important aspect in understanding your performance. Both the *percentage* of incorrect responses in a category and the total *number* of incorrect responses in a category should be carefully considered to make a complete interpretation of your performance.

You will recall that the competency category is a weighted element of the examination blueprint. This means that the number of questions on the exam from each competency category is set and that this number is not the same for each category. The distribution of the practice questions, by category, is as follows:

Professional Practice (PP)	17%
Nurse-Client Partnership (NCP)	12%
Health and Wellness (HW)	24%
Changes in Health (CH)	48%

Refer to the summary chart in chapter 2 to see the weighting of these competency categories on the CRNE.

It is important to consider both the percentage and the number of incorrect responses in a category. For example, if your performance profile chart shows that you obtained the highest percentage of incorrect answers in the Nurse-Client Partnership category in Table 1, you should keep in mind that a relatively small number of practice questions deal with Nurse-Client Partnership (23 questions out of the total of 200). Even if all your responses for that category were incorrect, the impact on your total score would be relatively small. On the other hand, a fairly small percentage of incorrect responses in the Changes in Health category (96 questions out of the total 200) can represent many questions on the exam. Consequently, improving your performance in this category by only a few percentage points can make a greater difference to your overall result.

Therefore, although a high percentage of incorrect responses in a competency category is certainly an indication of a weakness in that category, you need to consider both the competency category and the percentage representation on the exam when deciding where to place your study emphasis. Once you have determined in which competency categories you need to improve, you may wish to follow the four steps below.

1. Go to Appendix A and review the competencies in the categories identified as areas of weakness for you. This will give you an overview of the competencies that require your attention.

2. Review the questions for the competency categories where you need improvement. Include in your review both the questions you answered correctly and those you answered incorrectly. This will provide you with a more complete review of the content and the corresponding competencies that need improvement.

3. Be sure to read the rationales for the correct and incorrect responses to get a better understanding of your areas of weakness.

4. Look up the references cited (or other comparable references) for the questions you answered incorrectly. This can increase your understanding of material you may not have fully mastered.

TAXONOMY OF COGNITIVE ABILITY LEVELS

The interpretation approach given for the competency categories also applies to your results in the levels of cognitive ability because it also represents a weighted element of the blueprint. As a strategy for dealing with your identified area(s) of weakness, you may wish to follow the three steps below.

1. Verify your understanding of the levels of cognitive ability that are causing difficulties for you. This can be done by reviewing the definition of these levels (see chapter 2). You should also note the relative weight of each level.

2. Review all the questions that are classified within your weaker levels of cognitive ability. Include the questions that you answered correctly as well as those you answered incorrectly. This will provide you with a more complete review of the levels in question.

3. Look up the references cited (or other comparable references) to review more detailed information on the contents with which you had difficulty.

Finally, after having completed your review and preparation, you can retake the practice questions. By following the suggested strategies for dealing with your results, you should see an improvement in your overall score as well as in your performance profile results.

CHAPTER 7:
RATIONALES FOR THE PRACTICE QUESTIONS

■ RATIONALES

SAMPLE CASE RATIONALES

---

1. CORRECT ANSWER: 4

1. The nurse needs to know the client's baseline vital signs before making this judgment.

2. The nurse needs to know the client's baseline vital signs prior to contacting the physician.

3. The nurse needs to know the client's baseline vital signs before making judgments.

■ **4. A client's usual vital signs serve as a baseline for comparison and aid the nurse in making judgments about the client's condition.**

CLASSIFICATION

COMPETENCY CATEGORY: Changes in Health
TAXONOMIC LEVEL: Application
CLIENT TYPE: Individual
AGE GROUP: Older Adult

REFERENCES

Potter, P. A., Griffin Perry, A., Ross-Kerr, J. C., and Wood, M. J. (2006), p. 563.

Day, R. A., Paul, P., Williams, B., Smeltzer, S. C., and Bare, B. (2007), p. 65.

---

2. CORRECT ANSWER: 4

1. The nurse should assess the client's current understanding in order to determine his learning needs.

2. This does not prevent respiratory complications.

3. This position is contraindicated following a total hip replacement.

■ **4. This is an effective way to assess the client's current knowledge base in regards to preventing postoperative respiratory complications.**

CLASSIFICATION

COMPETENCY CATEGORY: Changes in Health
TAXONOMIC LEVEL: Application
CLIENT TYPE: Individual
AGE GROUP: Older Adult

REFERENCES

Potter, P. A., Griffin Perry, A., Ross-Kerr, J. C., and Wood, M. J. (2006), p. 220.

Mantik Lewis, S., McLean Heitkemper, M., Ruff Dirksen, S., Goldsworthy, S., and Barry, M. A. (2006), p. 47.

---

3. CORRECT ANSWER: 3

1. There should be no flexion of the hips in the postoperative period.

2. This is not contraindicated.

■ **3. Hip flexion greater than 90 degrees and adducting the legs increases the risk for hip dislocation following total hip replacement.**

4. This is not contraindicated.

CLASSIFICATION

COMPETENCY CATEGORY: Changes in Health
TAXONOMIC LEVEL: Application
CLIENT TYPE: Individual
AGE GROUP: Older Adult

REFERENCES

Black, J. M., and Hokanson Hawks, J. (2009), pp. 479-481.

Timby, B. K., and Smith, N. E. (2007), p. 1202.

---

4. CORRECT ANSWER: 2

1. Client should be informed that early ambulation reduces complications following major surgery.

■ 2. **This provides the client with a rationale for early ambulation and addresses the client's pain management concern.**

3. This does not provide a rationale for early ambulation or address the client's concerns about pain.

4. This does not provide a rationale for early ambulation and may not provide adequate pain control one day following major orthopaedic surgery.

CLASSIFICATION

COMPETENCY CATEGORY: Health and Wellness

TAXONOMIC LEVEL: Critical Thinking

CLIENT TYPE: Individual

AGE GROUP: Older Adult

REFERENCES

Mantik Lewis, S., McLean Heitkemper, M., Ruff Dirksen, S., Goldsworthy, S., and Barry, M. A. (2006), p. 409.

Black, J. M., and Hokanson Hawks, J. (2009), pp. 479-481.

5. CORRECT ANSWER: 3

1. This does not address signs and symptoms of impending heart failure.

2. This does not address signs and symptoms of impending heart failure.

■ 3. **The client is presenting with symptoms of impending heart failure that need to be addressed in a timely manner.**

4. This does not address signs and symptoms of impending heart failure.

CLASSIFICATION

COMPETENCY CATEGORY: Changes in Health

TAXONOMIC LEVEL: Critical Thinking

CLIENT TYPE: Individual

AGE GROUP: Older Adult

REFERENCES

Mantik Lewis, S., McLean Heitkemper, M., Ruff Dirksen, S., Goldsworthy, S., and Barry, M. A. (2006), p. 853.

Timby, B. K., and Smith, N. E. (2007), p. 519.

END OF SAMPLE CASE RATIONALES

CASE 1 RATIONALES

1. CORRECT ANSWER: 2

1. A PowerPoint presentation is not necessarily the best method to convey information.

■ 2. **Hands-on activities can be an effective learning tool.**

3. Listening does not use all of the methods for learning (i.e., visual kinesthetics).

4. This is an assessment method for learning and is not a method for conveying information.

CLASSIFICATION

COMPETENCY CATEGORY: Nurse-Client Partnership

TAXONOMIC LEVEL: Critical Thinking

CLIENT TYPE: Family

AGE GROUP: Young Adult

REFERENCES

Taylor, C., Lillis, C., LeMone, P., and Lynn, P. (2008), pp. 510-511.

Smith Murray, S., and Slone McKinney, E. (2006), p. 26.

2. CORRECT ANSWER: 1

■ 1. **Helping Mr. McKay practise comfort measures will increase his confidence to help his partner.**

2. His concern is to provide assistance to help his partner.

3. This does not deal with the issue of Mr. McKay wanting to support his partner.

4. The nurse should support Mr. McKay in the area of family support that he has requested.

CLASSIFICATION

COMPETENCY CATEGORY: Changes in Health

TAXONOMIC LEVEL: Critical Thinking

CLIENT TYPE: Family

AGE GROUP: Young Adult

REFERENCES

Smith Murray, S., and Slone McKinney, E. (2006), p. 235.

Wong, D. L., Perry, S. E., Hockenberry, M. J., Lowdermilk, D. L., and Wilson, D. (2006), pp. 516, 518.

3. CORRECT ANSWER: 2

1. This is normal output for an infant of this age.

■ 2. **The infant should breastfeed 8-12 times per 24 hours at this age. Infrequent breastfeeding can cause dehydration, which can lead to an infant waking less often.**

3. Mustard-coloured bowel movements are normal for an infant of this age.

4. Draining one breast per feed is encouraged to allow the higher fat hindmilk to be consumed.

CLASSIFICATION

COMPETENCY CATEGORY: Changes in Health

TAXONOMIC LEVEL: Critical Thinking

CLIENT TYPE: Family

AGE GROUP: Newborn and Infants

REFERENCES

Burns, C. E., Dunn, A. M., Brady, M. A., Barber Starr, N., and Blosser, C. G. (2009), p. 243.

Wong, D. L., Perry, S. E., Hockenberry, M. J., Lowdermilk, D. L., and Wilson, D. (2006), pp. 776-777.

4. CORRECT ANSWER: 4

1. This does not support the clients' decision. This infers that the clients need more information to make a decision.

2. This is not supportive of the clients' decision and could be perceived as coercion.

3. This solution does not address the issue because the clients already have the knowledge.

■ 4. **The nurse must accept their decision in a non-judgmental way. Formula knowledge is required to ensure proper infant nutrition.**

CLASSIFICATION

COMPETENCY CATEGORY: Nurse-Client Partnership

TAXONOMIC LEVEL: Application

CLIENT TYPE: Family

AGE GROUP: Newborn and Infants

REFERENCES

Taylor, C., Lillis, C., LeMone, P., and Lynn, P. (2008), p. 494.

Arnold, E. C., and Underman Boggs, K. (2007), p. 320.

5. CORRECT ANSWER: 1

■ 1. **Social connections through a support group can help develop new coping mechanisms.**

2. Both parents need support; care may be equal at this time.

3. This may not be practical or the best long-term solution.

4. While normalizing a situation can be useful, it does not address development of new coping skills.

CLASSIFICATION

COMPETENCY CATEGORY: Health and Wellness

TAXONOMIC LEVEL: Critical Thinking

CLIENT TYPE: Family

AGE GROUP: Young Adult

REFERENCES

Wong, D. L., Perry, S. E., Hockenberry, M. J., Lowdermilk, D. L., and Wilson, D. (2006), pp. 645-646, 901.

Craven, R. F., and Hirnle, C. J. (2009), p. 1307.

END OF CASE 1 RATIONALES

CASE 2 RATIONALES

6. CORRECT ANSWER: 3

1. Although this is important, the most important issue is preventing hypoglycemic shock.

2. Although this is important, it can be done when Mr. Parker's blood glucose is stabilized.

■ 3. **Immediate treatment must be given when hypoglycemia occurs. Hypoglycemia occurs when blood glucose falls to less than 2.7 to 3.3 mmol/L.**

4. Teaching strategies are important but are not the most appropriate treatment at this time.

CLASSIFICATION

COMPETENCY CATEGORY: Changes in Health

TAXONOMIC LEVEL: Critical Thinking

CLIENT TYPE: Individual

AGE GROUP: Middle Adult

REFERENCES

Black, J. M., and Hokanson Hawks, J. (2009), p. 411.

Day, R. A., Paul, P., Williams, B., Smeltzer, S. C. and Bare, B. (2007), p. 1183.

7. CORRECT ANSWER: 2

1. Low blood glucose does not impact hypertension.

■ 2. **Prolonged exposure to stress is linked to hypertension. Stress increases the peripheral vascular resistance and cardiac output, which stimulates the sympathetic nervous system. Over time, hypertension develops.**

3. This action may reduce stress and hypertension because Mr. Parker enjoys spending time with his children.

4. This is not the most significant factor in hypertension.

CLASSIFICATION

COMPETENCY CATEGORY: Health and Wellness

TAXONOMIC LEVEL: Critical Thinking

CLIENT TYPE: Individual

AGE GROUP: Middle Adult

REFERENCES

Black, J. M., and Hokanson Hawks, J. (2009), p. 1278.

Potter, P. A., Griffin Perry, A., Ross-Kerr, J. C., and Wood, M. J. (2006), p. 599.

8. CORRECT ANSWER: 3

1. This is taking accountability for nursing education away from the nurse and passing it on to the physician.

2. The priority is to get Mr. Parker's diabetes under control. A change in job may not manage his diabetes.

■ **3. Diet and exercise are important components in the care of clients with diabetes. Referral to a dietitian will assist in diabetes care and management.**

4. Although Mr. Parker might need to consult a counsellor for stress management at this time, this is not the most appropriate intervention.

CLASSIFICATION

COMPETENCY CATEGORY: Health and Wellness
TAXONOMIC LEVEL: Application
CLIENT TYPE: Individual
AGE GROUP: Middle Adult

REFERENCES

Black, J. M., and Hokanson Hawks, J. (2009), p. 1011.

Potter, P. A., Griffin Perry, A., Ross-Kerr, J. C., and Wood, M. J. (2006), pp. 1321, 1323.

9. CORRECT ANSWER: 3

1. Telling is a task-related approach, which is not client focused. There is no time for feedback with this approach.

2. Discovery is a useful technique with problem-solving.

■ **3. This approach involves the nurse and client in setting objectives and participating in the learning process together. There is the opportunity for discussion, feedback, mutual goal-setting and revision of the care plan.**

4. This is a formal method of instruction for presentation of content.

CLASSIFICATION

COMPETENCY CATEGORY: Changes in Health
TAXONOMIC LEVEL: Knowledge/Comprehension
CLIENT TYPE: Individual
AGE GROUP: Middle Adult

REFERENCES

Potter, P. A., Griffin Perry, A., Ross-Kerr, J. C., and Wood, M. J. (2006), p. 327.

Potter, P. A., and Griffin Perry, A. (2007), p. 188.

END OF CASE 2 RATIONALES

10. CORRECT ANSWER: 2

1. Organizing activities of daily living (ADLs) does not address the issue of fatigue, which is the factor that needs to be addressed.

■ **2. Balancing rest and activity allows the person to build tolerance and decrease related fatigue in performing ADLs.**

3. This does not change Mrs. Thompson's ability and brings in external resources. Moreover, this does not address the issues of overexertion and rest.

4. Passive exercises will help with muscle tone but will not decrease Mrs. Thompson's degree of fatigue.

CLASSIFICATION

COMPETENCY CATEGORY: Health and Wellness
TAXONOMIC LEVEL: Critical Thinking
CLIENT TYPE: Family
AGE GROUP: Middle Adult

REFERENCES

Day, R. A., Paul, P., Williams, B., Smeltzer, S. C., and Bare, B. (2007), p. 186.
Rice, R. (2006), p. 190.

11. CORRECT ANSWER: 2

1. This is relevant but not the initial step until more knowledge of the diagnosis is obtained.

■ **2. Evidence-informed practice requires the nurse to develop care plans based on research or expert opinion that supports the interventions.**

3. This is appropriate but not the initial step because case review needs to happen before further assessment is possible.

4. This does not ensure knowledge of chronic fatigue syndrome.

CLASSIFICATION

COMPETENCY CATEGORY: Professional Practice
TAXONOMIC LEVEL: Critical Thinking
CLIENT TYPE: Family
AGE GROUP: Middle Adult

REFERENCES

Craven, R. F., and Hirnle, C. J. (2009), pp. 42-43, 78.
Potter, P. A., and Griffin Perry, A. (2007), p. 31.

12. CORRECT ANSWER: 1

■ **1. The purpose of setting small, achievable goals is to increase the chance of success for each goal and thereby build confidence.**

2. This is not the priority action. The accomplishment of achievable goals is required to improve the client's self-esteem.

3. An evaluation plan is the final step of the problem-solving process.

4. This is premature.

CLASSIFICATION

COMPETENCY CATEGORY: Changes in Health
TAXONOMIC LEVEL: Application
CLIENT TYPE: Family
AGE GROUP: Middle Adult

REFERENCES

Ackley, B. J., and Ladwig, G. B. (2006), p. 518.
Potter, P. A., Griffin Perry, A., Ross-Kerr, J. C., and Wood, M. J. (2006), pp. 200-201.

13. CORRECT ANSWER: 4

1. There is no information provided about the strength of the family's social network. This might be a later action that is part of an overall plan.

2. This is important but does not answer the question about helping the family cope.

3. This is unrealistic because these services are not likely available for this type of client and if they were they would not address the coping skills of the family.

■ 4. **This involves everyone in the process. Controlling the stressors is the best way to reduce family stress.**

CLASSIFICATION

COMPETENCY CATEGORY: Health and Wellness
TAXONOMIC LEVEL: Critical Thinking
CLIENT TYPE: Family
AGE GROUP: Middle Adult

REFERENCES

Potter, P. A., Griffin Perry, A., Ross-Kerr, J. C., and Wood, M. J. (2006), p. 187.

Craven, R. F., and Hirnle, C. J. (2009), pp. 129-131.

14. CORRECT ANSWER: 2

1. These are indicators of depression.

■ 2. **These are some of the risk factors for self-inflicted injury (i.e., suicide).**

3. These are indicators of psychotic behaviour.

4. These are indicators of dementia.

CLASSIFICATION

COMPETENCY CATEGORY: Changes in Health
TAXONOMIC LEVEL: Application
CLIENT TYPE: Family
AGE GROUP: Middle Adult

REFERENCES

Austin, W., and Boyd, M. A. (2008), p. 372.

Potter, P. A., Griffin Perry, A., Ross-Kerr, J. C., and Wood, M. J. (2006), p. 390.

END OF CASE 3 RATIONALES

CASE 4 RATIONALES

15. CORRECT ANSWER: 1

■ 1. **The indirect Coombs' test is done on the mother; the direct test is done on the infant. Because the mother was sensitized (i.e., indirect Coombs' test was negative), she would not need the Rho(D) immune globulin treatment (Rhogam), but would need to be monitored closely (i.e., titres).**

2. Rh-negative people do not have the antigens.

3. These antibodies develop as an initial response but are too large to cross the placental barrier. It is the IgG and anti-D antibodies that cross the placenta and cause hemolysis of fetal red blood cells.

4. The serum still needs to be given because of the mixing of maternal and fetal blood during the delivery process (e.g., from damaged placental villi).

CLASSIFICATION

COMPETENCY CATEGORY: Health and Wellness
TAXONOMIC LEVEL: Knowledge/Comprehension
CLIENT TYPE: Individual
AGE GROUP: The Period Between Preconception and Birth

REFERENCES

Hockenberry, M. J., and Wilson, D. (2007), pp. 852-854.
Leonard Lowdermilk, D., and Perry, E. S. (2006), p. 911.

16. CORRECT ANSWER: 4

1. The risk of infection is minimal because there is no break in the scalp.

2. Swelling outside the cranium does not put the infant at risk for seizure activity.

3. Caput (swelling beneath the skin of the scalp) decreases within a couple of days.

■ 4. **A cephalhematoma does not cross the suture line and the blood is absorbed.**

CLASSIFICATION

COMPETENCY CATEGORY: Changes in Health
TAXONOMIC LEVEL: Application
CLIENT TYPE: Individual
AGE GROUP: Newborn and Infants

REFERENCES

Wong, D. L., Perry, S. E., Hockenberry, M. J., Lowdermilk, D. L., and Wilson, D. (2006), p. 698.
Murray, S. S., McKinney, E. S., and Gorrie, T. M. (2006), pp. 479-480.

17. CORRECT ANSWER: 1

■ 1. **Protection from sepsis, cold stress, hypoglycemia and acidosis can decrease the risks of hemolytic disease and kernicterus.**

2. Preventive measures in the antepartum stage have decreased the need for exchange transfusions.

3. The infant may have a weak positive antibody test because of the mother's sensitization.

4. A group and type test is done on umbilical cord blood but does not assess for antibodies.

CLASSIFICATION

COMPETENCY CATEGORY: Changes in Health

TAXONOMIC LEVEL: Critical Thinking

CLIENT TYPE: Family

AGE GROUP: Newborn and Infants

REFERENCES

Wong, D. L., Perry, S. E., Hockenberry, M. J., Lowdermilk, D. L., and Wilson, D. (2006), p. 853.

Murray, S. S., McKinney, E. S., and Gorrie, T. M. (2006), pp. 806-807.

END OF CASE 4 RATIONALES

CASE 5 RATIONALES

18. CORRECT ANSWER: 1

■ 1. **High-Fowler's position reduces the workload on the heart and decreases venous return.**

2. A physician's order would be required for oxygen therapy at a high flow rate.

3. Preparing for an IV infusion would be correct later on, but it is not appropriate as the initial action by the nurse.

4. Arranging for blood gases would not provide immediate relief; a physician's order would be required for treatment based on the analysis.

CLASSIFICATION

COMPETENCY CATEGORY: Changes in Health

TAXONOMIC LEVEL: Critical Thinking

CLIENT TYPE: Individual

AGE GROUP: Older Adult

REFERENCES

Day, R. A., Paul, P., Williams, B., Smeltzer, S. C., and Bare, B. (2007), p. 800.

Potter, P. A., Griffin Perry, A., Ross-Kerr, J. C., and Wood, M. J. (2006), p. 1103.

19. CORRECT ANSWER: 3

1. Synthetics contribute more than natural fibres to the build-up of static electricity, which is dangerous given the flammability of oxygen.

2. Properly grounded equipment, with no frayed cords, is safe to use.

■ 3. **To ensure that the equipment is operating safely (e.g., the correct amount of oxygen), the ports on the mask must be checked.**

4. There is no evidence that oil-based creams pose a safety risk to clients receiving oxygen therapy.

CLASSIFICATION

COMPETENCY CATEGORY: Health and Wellness

TAXONOMIC LEVEL: Application

CLIENT TYPE: Individual

AGE GROUP: Older Adult

REFERENCES

Day, R. A., Paul, P., Williams, B., Smeltzer, S. C., and Bare, B. (2007), pp. 606-608.

Potter, P. A., Griffin Perry, A., Ross-Kerr, J. C., and Wood, M. J. (2006), p. 1132.

20. CORRECT ANSWER: **1**

■ 1. **Heart rate will be affected by the medication and needs to be monitored and recorded so adjustments in dosage can be made.**

2. Blood pressure is not the primary characteristic that should be recorded with this medication.

3. Respiratory rate is not affected by this medication.

4. While activity level would alter the pulse rate, it is not a characteristic that needs to be recorded.

CLASSIFICATION

COMPETENCY CATEGORY: Changes in Health

TAXONOMIC LEVEL: Knowledge/Comprehension

CLIENT TYPE: Individual

AGE GROUP: Older Adult

REFERENCES

Lilley, L. L., Harrington, S., Snyder, J. S., and Swart, B. (2007), p. 354.

Ignatavicius, D. D., and Workman, M. L. (2006), p. 758.

21. CORRECT ANSWER: **2**

1. Weight stability demonstrates an anticipated response to therapy and is not important to report.

■ 2. **The dizziness implies a need for close monitoring to ensure Mr. Juliano's safety.**

3. Needing reminders is expected; this is not necessary to report.

4. Sleeping for short periods at regular intervals indicates an improvement in Mr. Juliano's sleep pattern over his admission status.

CLASSIFICATION

COMPETENCY CATEGORY: Changes in Health

TAXONOMIC LEVEL: Critical Thinking

CLIENT TYPE: Individual

AGE GROUP: Older Adult

REFERENCES

Potter, P. A., Griffin Perry, A., Ross-Kerr, J. C., and Wood, M. J. (2006), p. 236.

Mantik Lewis, S., McLean Heitkemper, M., Ruff Dirksen, S., Goldsworthy, S., and Barry, M. A. (2006), p. 803.

22. CORRECT ANSWER: **4**

1. There is no need to disturb Mr. Juliano when checking the intravenous rate on a regular basis.

2. Visits by familiar individuals contribute to orientation and meaningful sensory input.

3. Muted light would be more likely to cause sensory deprivation, rather than overload, in the older adult.

■ 4. **An unfamiliar, repetitious sound can contribute to sensory overload.**

CLASSIFICATION

COMPETENCY CATEGORY: Changes in Health

TAXONOMIC LEVEL: Application

CLIENT TYPE: Individual

AGE GROUP: Older Adult

REFERENCES

Potter, P. A., Griffin Perry, A., Ross-Kerr, J. C., and Wood, M. J. (2006), p. 1575.

Mantik Lewis, S., McLean Heitkemper, M., Ruff Dirksen, S., Goldsworthy, S., and Barry, M. A. (2006), p. 128.

END OF CASE 5 RATIONALES

23. CORRECT ANSWER: 1

■ 1. **This response provides Mrs. Kenny with information about ways to prevent foot problems from occurring as a result of neuropathy.**

2. This only defers the discussion and does not provide immediate information.

3. Providing research articles does not deal with the immediate discussion and assumes that Mrs. Kenny understands the research information.

4. This does not provide immediate teaching. Mrs. Kenny was diagnosed 15 years ago. She may not have the original information.

CLASSIFICATION

COMPETENCY CATEGORY: Health and Wellness

TAXONOMIC LEVEL: Application

CLIENT TYPE: Individual

AGE GROUP: Middle Adult

REFERENCES

Potter, P. A., Griffin Perry, A., Ross-Kerr, J. C., and Wood, M. J. (2006), p. 1576.

Smeltzer, S. C., Bare, B., Hinkle, J. L., and Cheever, K. H. (2007), pp. 1197-1200.

24. CORRECT ANSWER: 3

1. This does not allow Mrs. Kenny to make her own decisions.

2. Hyperglycemia does cause thirst and regular pop will raise blood sugars. The nurse is not exploring with Mrs. Kenny the reasons for choosing to drink cola.

■ 3. **This response identifies that Mrs. Kenny is thirsty because of her high blood sugars and allows Mrs. Kenny to explore her own reasons for this choice without the nurse's biases being introduced.**

4. The nurse is indicating to Mrs. Kenny that she made a poor choice before exploring her reasons for doing so. The list may be provided at some point, but only after these reasons have been explored.

CLASSIFICATION

COMPETENCY CATEGORY: Health and Wellness

TAXONOMIC LEVEL: Application

CLIENT TYPE: Individual

AGE GROUP: Middle Adult

REFERENCES

Potter, P. A., Griffin Perry, A., Ross-Kerr, J. C., and Wood, M. J. (2006), pp. 271-276.

Smeltzer, S. C., Bare, B., Hinkle, J. L., and Cheever, K. H. (2007), p. 1160.

25. CORRECT ANSWER: 3

1. Although this appointment is necessary to gain the support of the physician for insulin initiation, it is placing the responsibility for communication solely on Mrs. Kenny.

2. A discussion such as this is necessary, but the nurse is initiating the insulin, not the physician.

■ **3. This ensures that accurate information is communicated to the physician.**

4. This does not ensure that accurate information is provided to the physician. It also takes autonomy away from Mrs. Kenny.

CLASSIFICATION

COMPETENCY CATEGORY: Professional Practice

TAXONOMIC LEVEL: Application

CLIENT TYPE: Individual

AGE GROUP: Middle Adult

REFERENCES

Arnold, E. C., and Underman Boggs, K. (2007), pp. 483-484.

Hibberd, J. M., and Smith, D. L. (2006), pp. 520-521.

26. CORRECT ANSWER: 1

■ **1. This illustrates to Mrs. Kenny therapeutic understanding of her initial reluctance to use other sites but also highlights the importance of rotation of sites and opens the door to revisit this at a later time.**

2. This is not illustrating an understanding of Mrs. Kenny's hesitancy to use other sites and is using fear to change her mind.

3. This is identifying Mrs. Kenny's reluctance but is also taking this informed decision away from the client.

4. This is an inappropriate response as the nurse is telling Mrs. Kenny that she was not listening the first time.

CLASSIFICATION

COMPETENCY CATEGORY: Nurse-Client Partnership

TAXONOMIC LEVEL: Application

CLIENT TYPE: Individual

AGE GROUP: Middle Adult

REFERENCES

Smeltzer, S. C., Bare, B., Hinkle, J. L., and Cheever, K. H. (2007), p. 1181.

Arnold, E. C., and Underman Boggs, K. (2007), p. 200.

END OF CASE 6 RATIONALES

CASE 7 RATIONALES

27. CORRECT ANSWER: 2

1. Mrs. Chartrand will be less anxious if she can be assured her husband is receiving help.

■ **2. High-Fowler's with arms supported places Mr. Chartrand in an orthopneic position, which will help him breathe. This is a priority.**

3. Mr. Chartrand is too short of breath to interview for a complete history. This is not a priority.

4. Low-flow oxygen for COPD clients is required for hypoxemia during exacerbations. However, their hypoxic drive rules out administering too high a litre flow of oxygen.

CLASSIFICATION

COMPETENCY CATEGORY: Changes in Health
TAXONOMIC LEVEL: Critical Thinking
CLIENT TYPE: Individual
AGE GROUP: Older Adult

REFERENCES

Mantik Lewis, S., McLean Heitkemper, M., Ruff Dirksen, S., Goldsworthy, S., and Barry, M. A. (2006), p. 1838.

Black, J. M., and Hokanson Hawks, J. (2009), p. 1569.

28. CORRECT ANSWER: 2

1. A sedative can cause respiratory depression and may have triggered the current problem.

■ **2. Mr. Chartrand's anxiety is most likely related to his dyspnea; therefore, relaxation exercises are the most effective.**

3. Mr. Chartrand's oxygen concentration can interfere with his stimulus to breathe.

4. Mr. Chartrand is currently in the hospital, so this action is not appropriate.

CLASSIFICATION

COMPETENCY CATEGORY: Changes in Health
TAXONOMIC LEVEL: Critical Thinking
CLIENT TYPE: Individual
AGE GROUP: Older Adult

REFERENCES

Mantik Lewis, S., McLean Heitkemper, M., Ruff Dirksen, S., Goldsworthy, S., and Barry, M. A. (2006), p. 676.

Black, J. M., and Hokanson Hawks, J. (2009), p. 1590.

29. CORRECT ANSWER: 3

1. Although learning about breathing and positioning strategies is important, an assessment of the client's learning needs precedes teaching. Also, this does not correctly identify pursed-lips breathing.

2. Huff coughing will be a part of breathing strategies, but the client may already know how. His knowledge must be assessed first.

■ **3. The client has indicated a readiness to learn, but an assessment of current knowledge, coping strategies and learning needs must precede implementation.**

4. This is an implementation strategy. The client's needs must be assessed first.

CLASSIFICATION

COMPETENCY CATEGORY: Nurse-Client Partnership
TAXONOMIC LEVEL: Application
CLIENT TYPE: Individual
AGE GROUP: Older Adult

REFERENCES

Potter, P. A., Griffin Perry, A., Ross-Kerr, J. C., and Wood, M. J. (2006), p. 323.

Mantik Lewis, S., McLean Heitkemper, M., Ruff Dirksen, S., Goldsworthy, S., and Barry, M. A. (2006), pp. 682-685.

30. CORRECT ANSWER: **4**

1. This is not the correct information. Physical withdrawal can last for weeks to months.

2. This is not answering the client's concerns and is belittling.

3. This is providing false reassurance and is not addressing his concern.

■ **4. This provides correct information and directly addresses the client's question.**

CLASSIFICATION

COMPETENCY CATEGORY: Health and Wellness

TAXONOMIC LEVEL: Application

CLIENT TYPE: Family

AGE GROUP: Older Adult

REFERENCES

Mantik Lewis, S., McLean Heitkemper, M., Ruff Dirksen, S., Goldsworthy, S., and Barry, M. A. (2006), p. 181.

Potter, P. A., Griffin Perry, A., Ross-Kerr, J. C., and Wood, M. J. (2006), p. 275.

31. CORRECT ANSWER: **1**

■ **1. This is factual and answers the question in simple terms. The nurse should wait for a response before continuing.**

2. The nurse must verify first that the client wants to know the effect of this complication.

3. COPD leads to structural and functional damage in the lungs.

4. This describes pulmonary embolus.

CLASSIFICATION

COMPETENCY CATEGORY: Changes in Health

TAXONOMIC LEVEL: Application

CLIENT TYPE: Individual

AGE GROUP: Older Adult

REFERENCES

Mantik Lewis, S., McLean Heitkemper, M., Ruff Dirksen, S., Goldsworthy, S., and Barry, M. A. (2006), p. 672.

Mattson Porth, C. (2006), pp. 554, 712-713.

END OF CASE 7 RATIONALES

CASE 8 RATIONALES

32. CORRECT ANSWER: **2**

1. A gown and mask are required with anticipated contact with a client, contaminated items or within one metre (three feet) of the client.

■ **2. Droplet and contact precautions are required.**

3. A gown and mask are required with anticipated contact with a client, contaminated items or within one metre (three feet) of the client.

4. The mask is not required outside of the client's room.

CLASSIFICATION

COMPETENCY CATEGORY: Health and Wellness

TAXONOMIC LEVEL: Application

CLIENT TYPE: Group, Population, Community

AGE GROUP: Not applicable

REFERENCES

Leeseberg Stamler, L., and Yiu, L. (2008), pp. 143-147.

Potter, P. A., Griffin Perry, A., Ross-Kerr, J. C., and Wood, M. J. (2006), p. 807.

33. CORRECT ANSWER: 3

1. Alcohol-based hand sanitizers are effective unless hands are visibly soiled.
2. Alcohol-based hand sanitizers decrease skin irritation and drying. Emollients are added to alcohol-based hand sanitizers to prevent drying of the skin.
■ **3. Alcohol-based hand sanitizers are effective for most clinical situations.**
4. Influenza virus is not spore-forming.

CLASSIFICATION

COMPETENCY CATEGORY: Health and Wellness
TAXONOMIC LEVEL: Knowledge/Comprehension
CLIENT TYPE: Group, Population, Community
AGE GROUP: Not applicable

REFERENCES

Potter, P. A., Griffin Perry, A., Ross-Kerr, J. C., and Wood, M. J. (2006), pp. 800-801.
Smeltzer, S. C., Bare, B., Hinkle, J. L., and Cheever, K. H. (2007), p. 2136.

34. CORRECT ANSWER: 2

1. This does not address the isolation concerns and sends volunteers back into the community.
■ **2. These clients are not cognitively able to understand the need to stay in their room. Their emotional and social needs still need to be met.**
3. This is an unrealistic expectation of families.
4. It is unrealistic to move residents with dementia off the unit.

CLASSIFICATION

COMPETENCY CATEGORY: Professional Practice
TAXONOMIC LEVEL: Critical Thinking
CLIENT TYPE: Group, Population, Community
AGE GROUP: Not applicable

REFERENCES

Potter, P. A., Griffin Perry, A., Ross-Kerr, J. C., and Wood, M. J. (2006), p. 806.
Mattson Porth, C. (2006), p. 663.

35. CORRECT ANSWER: 3

1. This is defensive and does not address the nurses' feelings or lead to a collaborative discussion of the outbreak.
2. This deflects the issue and does not acknowledge the nurses' concerns.
■ **3. Schedule a time when everybody is calm and is meeting for a common goal.**
4. This does not allow the nurses to express their issues or concerns.

CLASSIFICATION

COMPETENCY CATEGORY: Professional Practice
TAXONOMIC LEVEL: Application
CLIENT TYPE: Group, Population, Community
AGE GROUP: Not applicable

REFERENCES

Wilkinson, J. M., and Van Leuven, K. (2007), p. 966.
Austin, W., and Boyd, M. A. (2008), pp. 186-187.

END OF CASE 8 RATIONALES

36. CORRECT ANSWER: 4

1. High pH indicates alkalosis.

2. pH and bicarbonate would be low in metabolic acidosis.

3. PCO_2 would be low in respiratory alkalosis.

■ **4. High pH indicates alkalosis, and high bicarbonate indicates metabolic alkalosis.**

CLASSIFICATION

COMPETENCY CATEGORY: Changes in Health

TAXONOMIC LEVEL: Critical Thinking

CLIENT TYPE: Individual

AGE GROUP: Middle Adult

REFERENCES

Mantik Lewis, S., McLean Heitkemper, M., Ruff Dirksen, S., Goldsworthy, S., and Barry, M. A. (2006), p. 358.

Day, R. A., Paul, P., Williams, B., Smeltzer, S. C., and Bare, B. (2007), pp. 285-287.

37. CORRECT ANSWER: 3

1. The tube does not need to be removed and replaced. Actions to correct the problem will prevent unnecessary stress to Ms. Pinchant.

2. The blue pigtail is the vent lumen. Obstruction to this tube may allow excess suction that can damage the gastric mucosa.

■ **3. The blue pigtail is the vent lumen. If it falls below the waist, it acts as a siphon.**

4. The blue pigtail is the vent lumen. It should be cleared with insertion of air if needed.

CLASSIFICATION

COMPETENCY CATEGORY: Changes in Health

TAXONOMIC LEVEL: Critical Thinking

CLIENT TYPE: Individual

AGE GROUP: Middle Adult

REFERENCES

Day, R. A., Paul, P., Williams, B., Smeltzer, S. C., and Bare, B. (2007), p. 991.

Black, J. M., and Hokanson Hawks, J. (2005), p. 745.

38. CORRECT ANSWER: 2

1. The client's concerns are a normal reaction and do not require a psychologist at this point.

■ **2. Referral to a well-adjusted ostomate can be reassuring and informative. Also, it involves Ms. Pinchant in meeting her needs.**

3. The ostomy support group is a good resource but would not meet her immediate needs for assistance.

4. This is judgmental and may provide the client false reassurance.

CLASSIFICATION

COMPETENCY CATEGORY: Changes in Health

TAXONOMIC LEVEL: Critical Thinking

CLIENT TYPE: Individual

AGE GROUP: Middle Adult

REFERENCES

Potter, P. A., Griffin Perry, A., Ross-Kerr, J. C., and Wood, M. J. (2006), p. 1404.

Day, R. A., Paul, P., Williams, B., Smeltzer, S. C and Bare, B. (2007), p. 1066.

39. CORRECT ANSWER: **3**

1. The change in colour suggests ischemia. The surgeon should be notified. Action is required to restore blood flow to the stoma.

2. While the information should be charted, the findings suggest ischemia. The surgeon should be notified. Action is required to restore blood flow to the stoma.

■ **3. The colour change suggests ischemia. The surgeon should be notified. Action is required to restore blood flow to the stoma.**

4. The colour change suggests ischemia. The surgeon should be notified. Action is required to restore blood flow to the stoma.

CLASSIFICATION

COMPETENCY CATEGORY: Changes in Health

TAXONOMIC LEVEL: Critical Thinking

CLIENT TYPE: Individual

AGE GROUP: Middle Adult

REFERENCES

Day, R. A., Paul, P., Williams, B., Smeltzer, S. C., and Bare, B. (2007), p. 1067.

Mantik Lewis, S., McLean Heitkemper, M., Ruff Dirksen, S., Graber O'Brien, P., and Bucher, L. (2007), p. 1071.

40. CORRECT ANSWER: **4**

1. Although this is an important assurance, the nurse needs to know why the student is reluctant.

2. The nurse is making a presumption that the student views this as an unpleasant procedure.

3. The nurse is presuming that the student is not willing to take on new learning opportunities without knowing the reason for the student's reluctance.

■ **4. This option enables the nurse to assess the reason for the student's reluctance in order to provide meaningful feedback. This also reflects a collaborative approach.**

CLASSIFICATION

COMPETENCY CATEGORY: Professional Practice

TAXONOMIC LEVEL: Critical Thinking

CLIENT TYPE: Not applicable

AGE GROUP: Not applicable

REFERENCES

Gottlieb, L. N., and Feeley, N. (2006), p. 35.

Day, R. A., Paul, P., Williams, B., Smeltzer, S. C., and Bare, B. (2007), p. 46.

END OF CASE 9 RATIONALES

41. CORRECT ANSWER: **3**

1. An incorrect formula calculation was used or an error was made in the calculation.

2. An incorrect formula calculation was used or an error was made in the calculation.

■ **3. The correct formula is dose available/volume of solution available = dose desired/volume required.**

4. An incorrect formula calculation was used or an error was made in the calculation.

CLASSIFICATION

COMPETENCY CATEGORY: Changes in Health

TAXONOMIC LEVEL: Application

CLIENT TYPE: Individual

AGE GROUP: Middle Adult

REFERENCES

Potter, P. A., Griffin Perry, A., Ross-Kerr, J. C., and Wood, M. J. (2006), p. 844.

Elkin, M. K., Griffin Perry, A., and Potter, P. A. (2007), pp. 371-372.

42. CORRECT ANSWER: **4**

1. Removal and replacement of the catheter would be done only after other less invasive actions have failed. This is an appropriate catheter size.

2. Irrigating the catheter would not be done first. This procedure usually requires a physician's order.

3. Mr. James has a closed drainage system that should not be opened.

■ **4. The nurse should first check for an external obstruction affecting the drainage tube before taking other actions. Urinary output should be 30 mL/h.**

CLASSIFICATION

COMPETENCY CATEGORY: Changes in Health

TAXONOMIC LEVEL: Critical Thinking

CLIENT TYPE: Individual

AGE GROUP: Middle Adult

REFERENCES

Potter, P. A., Griffin Perry, A., Ross-Kerr, J. C., and Wood, M. J. (2006), pp. 1371-1372.

Elkin, M. K., Griffin Perry, A., and Potter, P. A. (2007), pp. 744-746.

43. CORRECT ANSWER: **3**

1. The rate should not be constant. For the first 15 minutes the transfusion should be infused slowly, and then the rate should be increased.

2. A slow infusion will not avoid a transfusion reaction and may interfere with completing the transfusion on time.

■ **3. Most transfusion reactions occur within the first few minutes so transfusion rates are increased after 15 minutes.**

4. The pressure appliance damages the red blood cells and is used only in emergencies.

CLASSIFICATION

COMPETENCY CATEGORY: Changes in Health

TAXONOMIC LEVEL: Application

CLIENT TYPE: Individual

AGE GROUP: Middle Adult

REFERENCES

Potter, P. A., Griffin Perry, A., Ross-Kerr, J. C., and Wood, M. J. (2006), pp. 1202-1203.

Day, R. A., Paul, P., Williams, B., Smeltzer, S. C., and Bare, B. (2007), p. 931.

44. CORRECT ANSWER: 2

1. It is unrealistic to ask a relative to remain with Mr. James 24 hours a day.

■ **2. The nurse should first make an assessment of Mr. James' requirements for supervision and then meet them as necessary.**

3. This will not ensure that he is safe.

4. Labelling Mr. James' bed with a sign represents a breach of confidentiality and shows a lack of respect.

CLASSIFICATION

COMPETENCY CATEGORY: Health and Wellness

TAXONOMIC LEVEL: Application

CLIENT TYPE: Individual

AGE GROUP: Middle Adult

REFERENCES

Potter, P. A., Griffin Perry, A., Ross-Kerr, J. C., and Wood, M. J. (2006), p. 1644.

Elkin, M. K., Griffin Perry, A., and Potter, P. A. (2007), p. 489.

45. CORRECT ANSWER: 4

1. A saline enema is not likely to facilitate evacuation of the large, hard mass.

2. The use of a laxative would cause bowel cramping without removing the fecal mass from the rectum.

3. The problem is fecal impaction, not constipation.

■ **4. The appropriate method for fecal disimpaction is to remove the feces manually with a lubricated, gloved finger.**

CLASSIFICATION

COMPETENCY CATEGORY: Changes in Health

TAXONOMIC LEVEL: Application

CLIENT TYPE: Individual

AGE GROUP: Middle Adult

REFERENCES

Potter, P. A., Griffin Perry, A., Ross-Kerr, J. C., and Wood, M. J. (2006), p. 1358.

Elkin, M. K., Griffin Perry, A., and Potter, P. A. (2007), p. 722.

END OF CASE 10 RATIONALES

CASE 11 RATIONALES

46. CORRECT ANSWER: 1

■ **1. Narcotics may be given to decrease intraoperative anesthetic requirements and to increase the client's comfort from pain.**

2. Although this is important, it is not the priority.

3. The client is going into shock, so the priority is to get the client into the operating room where the surgeon will see directly what is happening.

4. Although this is necessary, decreasing the client's pain first will relax the client, who will have less constricted blood vessels for an easier phlebotomy.

CLASSIFICATION

COMPETENCY CATEGORY: Changes in Health

TAXONOMIC LEVEL: Critical Thinking

CLIENT TYPE: Individual

AGE GROUP: Young Adult

REFERENCES

Mantik Lewis, S., McLean Heitkemper, M., Ruff Dirksen, S., Goldsworthy, S., and Barry, M. A. (2006), p. 376.

Griffin Perry, A., and Potter, P. A. (2006), p. 1182.

47. CORRECT ANSWER: **2**

1. Although this is a good supplemental way to communicate, the verbal report is not a part of the medical record.

■ **2. The checklist is a concise, thorough tool for communicating with the operating room that covers both objective and descriptive information.**

3. Although knowing when medication was given is important, the information from these documents is captured concisely on the preoperative checklist.

4. Although valuable for general information, a unique perioperative nursing care plan is developed during the client's event in the operating room.

CLASSIFICATION

COMPETENCY CATEGORY: Professional Practice

TAXONOMIC LEVEL: Application

CLIENT TYPE: Individual

AGE GROUP: Young Adult

REFERENCES

Griffin Perry, A., and Potter, P. A. (2006), p. 1182.

Potter, P. A., Griffin Perry, A., Ross-Kerr, J. C., and Wood, M. J. (2006), p. 254.

48. CORRECT ANSWER: **3**

1. Baseline vitals need to be monitored immediately prior to blood administration.

2. A large-bore needle and appropriate solution should be part of the assessment, not just the IV line.

■ **3. This is the first step to do once it is established that a transfusion is required.**

4. Although it is necessary to know the client's blood type, blood is ordered on the basis of the client's specific crossmatch and not ordered by blood type.

CLASSIFICATION

COMPETENCY CATEGORY: Changes in Health

TAXONOMIC LEVEL: Critical Thinking

CLIENT TYPE: Individual

AGE GROUP: Young Adult

REFERENCES

Griffin Perry, A., and Potter, P. A. (2006), p. 970.

Mantik Lewis, S., McLean Heitkemper, M., Ruff Dirksen, S., Goldsworthy, S., and Barry, M. A. (2006), p. 756.

49. CORRECT ANSWER: **4**

1. Although it is important to concentrate on the task at hand, this response does not encourage inquiries from the client and family members.

2. This is factual information but does not deal with Mr. Wylder's concerns.

3. This is only a part of the factual information. Teaching should take into consideration the client's and family members' distress.

■ **4. This allows the nurse to devote undivided attention to the couple and explain in terms that a distressed person can assimilate during a crisis.**

CLASSIFICATION

COMPETENCY CATEGORY: Nurse-Client Partnership

TAXONOMIC LEVEL: Application

CLIENT TYPE: Family

AGE GROUP: Young Adult

REFERENCES

Day, R. A., Paul, P., Williams, B., Smeltzer, S. C. and Bare, B. (2007), p. 1411.

Potter, P. A., Griffin Perry, A., Ross-Kerr, J. C., and Wood, M. J. (2006), pp. 271-274.

END OF CASE 11 RATIONALES

50. CORRECT ANSWER: **2**

1. It is true that a child will be at risk of strangulation with something around her neck, but the child should not be left alone. The nurse and mother could discuss a plan to ensure this will not happen.

■ **2. This shows respect for different cultural beliefs. There is no judgment implied and this will not interfere with current treatments.**

3. This does not show respect for different cultural beliefs.

4. This is not addressing the issue.

CLASSIFICATION

COMPETENCY CATEGORY: Nurse-Client Partnership

TAXONOMIC LEVEL: Critical Thinking

CLIENT TYPE: Family

AGE GROUP: Newborn and Infants

REFERENCES

Pillitteri, A. (2007), p. 1227.

Wong, D. L., Perry, S. E., Hockenberry, M. J., Lowdermilk, D. L., and Wilson, D. (2006), p. 918.

51. CORRECT ANSWER: **1**

■ **1. A respiratory assessment while asleep is more accurate.**

2. Spreading activities disrupts a child's sleep/rest pattern.

3. Infants are generally positioned on their back.

4. Lights being off poses a safety risk.

CLASSIFICATION

COMPETENCY CATEGORY: Changes in Health

TAXONOMIC LEVEL: Critical Thinking

CLIENT TYPE: Individual

AGE GROUP: Newborn and Infants

REFERENCES

Pillitteri, A. (2007), pp. 1095, 1227.

Wong, D. L., Perry, S. E., Hockenberry, M. J., Lowdermilk, D. L., and Wilson, D. (2006), p. 1443.

52. CORRECT ANSWER: **3**

1. Emma's condition is not worsening.

2. Although Emma's temperature is elevated, this is not the reason for the increased HR, restlessness and tremors.

■ **3. Tachycardia, restlessness and tremors are the most common side effects of salbutamol (Ventolin). Emma's chest has improved air entry, decreased adventitious sounds and acceptable oxygenation.**

4. Restlessness is not expected.

CLASSIFICATION

COMPETENCY CATEGORY: Changes in Health

TAXONOMIC LEVEL: Critical Thinking

CLIENT TYPE: Individual

AGE GROUP: Newborn and Infants

REFERENCES

Craven, R. F., and Hirnle, C. J. (2009), p. 837.

Pillitteri, A. (2007), p. 1261.

53. CORRECT ANSWER: 2

1. This would help if both Michael and Emma had respiratory syncytial virus (RSV), then one nurse could care for the two children, but this would leave three other clients not cared for.

■ 2. **This demonstrates leadership skills and accountability to clients. The nurse is also aware of personal abilities and evaluates realistic expectations.**

3. This does not address the immediate problem. The nurse must act upon the situation immediately.

4. This is not a solution because the nurse has not considered safety issues.

CLASSIFICATION

COMPETENCY CATEGORY: Professional Practice

TAXONOMIC LEVEL: Critical Thinking

CLIENT TYPE: Group, Population, Community

AGE GROUP: Newborn and Infants

REFERENCES

Craven, R. F., and Hirnle, C. J. (2009), p. 102.

Potter, P. A., Griffin Perry, A., Ross-Kerr, J. C., and Wood, M. J. (2006), p. 156.

END OF CASE 12 RATIONALES

CASE 13 RATIONALES

54. CORRECT ANSWER: 1

■ 1. **The oliguric phase of acute renal failure can include congestive heart failure.**

2. Hypovolemia is a finding in the diuretic phase of acute renal failure.

3. Postural hypotension is a manifestation possible in the diuretic phase of acute renal failure.

4. Clients in the oliguric phase of acute renal failure are prone to fluid volume excess, not deficit.

CLASSIFICATION

COMPETENCY CATEGORY: Changes in Health

TAXONOMIC LEVEL: Critical Thinking

CLIENT TYPE: Individual

AGE GROUP: Older Adult

REFERENCES

Mantik Lewis, S., McLean Heitkemper, M., Ruff Dirksen, S., Goldsworthy, S., and Barry, M. A. (2006), pp. 1217-1218.

Day, R. A., Paul, P, Williams, B., Smeltzer, S. C., and Bare, B. (2007), pp. 1326-1328.

55. CORRECT ANSWER: **3**

1. Clients in the oliguric phase are on fluid restrictions and most are not able to tolerate oral feedings.

2. Clients need to be weighed only daily.

■ **3. Drowsiness is a symptom of acute renal failure, and side rails should be left up for safety reasons.**

4. Strict bedrest is recommended during the oliguric phase of acute renal failure.

CLASSIFICATION

COMPETENCY CATEGORY: Changes in Health
TAXONOMIC LEVEL: Critical Thinking
CLIENT TYPE: Individual
AGE GROUP: Older Adult

REFERENCES

Potter, P. A., Griffin Perry, A., Ross-Kerr, J. C., and Wood, M. J. (2006), pp. 976-977, 979-980.

Day, R. A., Paul, P., Williams, B., Smeltzer, S. C., and Bare, B. (2007), p. 1330.

56. CORRECT ANSWER: **2**

1. It is important to turn and position these clients because they are prone to skin breakdown; however, it is not necessary to do this q.1h.

■ **2. Measuring urinary output is crucial in the management of acute renal failure. All observations of the client's state of hydration need to be recorded so that hour-to-hour and day-to-day comparisons can be made.**

3. It is important to do deep breathing exercises because these clients can progress to congestive heart failure; however, it is not necessary to do this q.1h.

4. Edema may be present but it is not necessary to assess q.1h.

CLASSIFICATION

COMPETENCY CATEGORY: Changes in Health
TAXONOMIC LEVEL: Application
CLIENT TYPE: Individual
AGE GROUP: Older Adult

REFERENCES

Mantik Lewis, S., McLean Heitkemper, M., Ruff Dirksen, S., Goldsworthy, S., and Barry, M. A. (2006), pp. 1217-1218.

Day, R. A., Paul, P., Williams, B., Smeltzer, S. C., and Bare, B. (2007), pp. 1326-1328.

57. CORRECT ANSWER: **3**

1. Although the nurse should call the physician, it is not the first response.

2. This response is inappropriate because the nurse is suggesting that Mrs. Kirsh is at fault, without addressing her apprehension.

■ **3. This is the most appropriate response because the nurse is responding to Mrs. Kirsh's feelings and showing support in a calm manner.**

4. This response is inappropriate because it does not take Mrs. Kirsh's anxiety into account.

CLASSIFICATION

COMPETENCY CATEGORY: Nurse-Client Partnership
TAXONOMIC LEVEL: Critical Thinking
CLIENT TYPE: Individual
AGE GROUP: Older Adult

REFERENCES

Arnold, E. C., and Underman Boggs, K. (2007), pp. 205-209.

Riley, J. B. (2008), pp. 24-26.

58. CORRECT ANSWER: **3**

1. Changes should be reported immediately. Charting may not be done until late in the shift.

2. Rechecking the float nurse's assessment is an inappropriate use of the time of the nurse-in-charge.

■ **3. Reviewing with the float nurse what should be assessed and reported is important because it ensures that the float nurse will assess and report relevant observations immediately.**

4. Asking the nurse working in the next room to be available to the float nurse will not ensure that the float nurse will assess and report relevant observations immediately.

CLASSIFICATION

COMPETENCY CATEGORY: Professional Practice

TAXONOMIC LEVEL: Application

CLIENT TYPE: Individual

AGE GROUP: Older Adult

REFERENCES

Potter, P. A., Griffin Perry, A., Ross-Kerr, J. C., and Wood, M. J. (2006), pp. 152-153.

Day, R. A., Paul, P., Williams, B., Smeltzer, S. C and Bare, B. (2007), p. 1330.

59. CORRECT ANSWER: **3**

1. Providing milkshakes t.i.d. is inappropriate because clients in acute renal failure should eat a low-protein, high-carbohydrate, high-fat diet. Milkshakes are high in protein and therefore contraindicated.

2. Ensuring Mrs. Kirsh's privacy during meals is inappropriate because people tend to eat better in a social group setting than by themselves.

■ **3. Appetite is often best in the morning and deteriorates gradually throughout the day. Therefore, a high-calorie breakfast should be encouraged.**

4. This does not ensure food and fluid needs are met.

END OF CASE 13 RATIONALES

CLASSIFICATION

COMPETENCY CATEGORY: Changes in Health

TAXONOMIC LEVEL: Application

CLIENT TYPE: Individual

AGE GROUP: Older Adult

REFERENCES

Mantik Lewis, S., McLean Heitkemper, M., Ruff Dirksen, S., Goldsworthy, S., and Barry, M. A. (2006), p. 1222.

Day, R. A., Paul, P., Williams, B., Smeltzer, S. C and Bare, B. (2007), p. 1330.

60. CORRECT ANSWER: 2

1. This response may not be an accurate representation of Kyle's feelings.

■ 2. **The nurse is attempting to identify Kyle's feelings and attitudes that are the barrier to his ability to communicate.**

3. By returning later, the nurse avoids the issue of Kyle's communication problem. Delaying action does not assist in identifying the communication barrier.

4. The nurse is being defensive, which will likely increase the communication barrier.

CLASSIFICATION

COMPETENCY CATEGORY: Nurse-Client Partnership

TAXONOMIC LEVEL: Application

CLIENT TYPE: Individual

AGE GROUP: Adolescent

REFERENCES

Riley, J. B. (2008), p. 26.

Varcolis, E. M., Carson, V. B., and Shoemaker, N. C. (2006), p. 189.

61. CORRECT ANSWER: 1

■ 1. **Refraining from discussing Kyle's care with David ensures Kyle's right to confidentiality.**

2. It is not necessary to refrain from caring for Kyle simply because the nurse may have access to personal knowledge about him. Confidentiality is not breached by providing care.

3. The nurse should not discuss a client with anyone who is not on the health-care team.

4. The principal is not a member of the health-care team and should not be provided with information on Kyle's progress.

CLASSIFICATION

COMPETENCY CATEGORY: Professional Practice

TAXONOMIC LEVEL: Application

CLIENT TYPE: Group, Population, Community

AGE GROUP. Adolescent

REFERENCES

Potter, P. A., Griffin Perry, A., Ross-Kerr, J. C., and Wood, M. J. (2006), p. 98.

Canadian Nurses Association. (2008), pp. 15-16.

62. CORRECT ANSWER: 1

■ 1. **Encouraging Kyle to verbalize his reasons for refusing to attend group therapy is the first step in assessing the problem of non-compliance.**

2. Discussing Kyle's refusal with his mother and soliciting her help to encourage him to attend therapy sessions does not address the reason why Kyle is refusing to attend group therapy.

3. Informing Kyle of the need to attend group therapy does not address the reason for his non-compliance.

4. Telling Kyle that there is an activity that he would probably enjoy is a form of manipulation.

CLASSIFICATION

COMPETENCY CATEGORY: Changes in Health

TAXONOMIC LEVEL: Critical Thinking

CLIENT TYPE: Family

AGE GROUP: Adolescent

REFERENCES

Canadian Nurses Association. (2008), pp. 11-12.

Potter, P. A., Griffin Perry, A., Ross-Kerr, J. C., and Wood, M. J. (2006), pp. 106-107.

63. CORRECT ANSWER: 1

■ 1. **The nurse has accepted constructive feedback, conducted further assessment and incorporated the colleagues' suggestion, if applicable, into the plan of care.**

2. The nurse is listening but is ignoring potentially valuable input from colleagues.

3. Seeking out learning opportunities is an overreaction to constructive feedback. There is no information to suggest that the nurse is lacking in psychiatric nursing skills.

4. Lack of resources should not be a reason for not being involved in the plan of care.

CLASSIFICATION

COMPETENCY CATEGORY: Changes in Health

TAXONOMIC LEVEL: Application

CLIENT TYPE: Family

AGE GROUP: Adolescent

REFERENCES

Varcolis, E. M., Carson, V. B., and Shoemaker, N. C. (2006), p. 6.

Keltner, N. L., Bostrom, C. E., and Hilyard Schwecke, L. (2007), p. 24.

64. CORRECT ANSWER: 3

1. Assuring Kyle of the other nurses' qualifications does not coordinate the care plan to be implemented by other members of the nursing staff.

2. Admission as an in-patient would be indicated only if Kyle's condition deteriorated and not because the nurse was not available.

■ 3. **By discussing the treatment plan, the nurse has coordinated the care plan with other members of the nursing staff as well as with Kyle and his mother.**

4. The nurse is validating that Kyle and his mother will be able to follow through on the treatment plan, but no provision has been made for continuity of care with other members of the nursing staff.

CLASSIFICATION

COMPETENCY CATEGORY: Changes in Health

TAXONOMIC LEVEL: Application

CLIENT TYPE: Family

AGE GROUP: Adolescent

REFERENCES

Varcolis, E. M., Carson, V. B., and Shoemaker, N. C. (2006), p. 93.

Keltner, N. L., Bostrom, C. E., and Hilyard Schwecke, L. (2007), p. 115.

65. CORRECT ANSWER: 4

1. An agency survey may not address Kyle's and his mother's specific needs and, therefore, is not a good measure of their satisfaction with nursing care.

2. Discussing their satisfaction with the individual nurses at the agency is inappropriate because it is nursing care that should be evaluated and not the individual nurses.

3. Evidence of suicidal ideation is only one aspect of Kyle's progress and is not necessarily a measurement of the client's and family's satisfaction.

■ 4. **If mutually agreed upon goals have been met, it is an indication that Kyle and his mother are satisfied with the nursing care provided.**

CLASSIFICATION

COMPETENCY CATEGORY: Changes in Health

TAXONOMIC LEVEL: Application

CLIENT TYPE: Family

AGE GROUP: Adolescent

REFERENCES

Varcolis, E. M., Carson, V. B., and Shoemaker, N. C. (2006), p. 152.

Keltner, N. L., Bostrom, C. E., and Hilyard Schwecke, L. (2007), p. 115.

END OF CASE 14 RATIONALES

CASE 15 RATIONALES

66. CORRECT ANSWER: 1

■ 1. **Checking for placement determines whether the tube is in the stomach before feeding.**

2. Mrs. Peters should be placed in a right lateral position or Fowler's position to facilitate movement of the feeding from the stomach into the small intestine.

3. Changing the tubing is not necessary before each feeding.

4. Water is instilled after feeding to maintain patency; instilling before ascertaining placement of the tube may introduce water to the lungs.

CLASSIFICATION

COMPETENCY CATEGORY: Changes in Health

TAXONOMIC LEVEL: Knowledge/Comprehension

CLIENT TYPE: Individual

AGE GROUP: Adult of Advanced Age

REFERENCES

Day, R. A., Paul, P., Williams, B., Smeltzer, S. C., and Bare, B. (2007), pp. 992-993.

Potter, P. A., Griffin Perry, A., Ross-Kerr, J. C., and Wood, M. J. (2006), pp. 1304-1305.

67. CORRECT ANSWER: 4

1. The activity room may provide too much stimulation, given Mrs. Peters' current health status.

2. Removing family photos will decrease sensory stimulation and the opportunity for conversation.

3. Clocks and calendars promote orientation, not sensory stimulation.

■ **4. Talking with Mrs. Peters will encourage her to use her senses.**

CLASSIFICATION

COMPETENCY CATEGORY: Changes in Health

TAXONOMIC LEVEL: Application

CLIENT TYPE: Individual

AGE GROUP: Adult of Advanced Age

REFERENCES

Potter, P. A., Griffin Perry, A., Ross-Kerr, J. C., and Wood, M. J. (2006), pp. 261-262.

Day, R. A., Paul, P, Williams, B., Smeltzer, S. C and Bare, B. (2007), p. 1865.

68. CORRECT ANSWER: 1

■ **1. The nurse should assess Mrs. Peters' orientation status first in order to determine the cause of her confusion.**

2. Sedation may increase confusion in the adult of advanced age. There is no indication for sedation at this time.

3. Encouraging Mrs. Peters to express her concerns may be a subsequent intervention.

4. Encouraging Mrs. Peters to participate in her plan of care is not possible given her confused state.

CLASSIFICATION

COMPETENCY CATEGORY: Changes in Health

TAXONOMIC LEVEL: Critical Thinking

CLIENT TYPE: Individual

AGE GROUP: Adult of Advanced Age

REFERENCES

Potter, P. A., Griffin Perry, A., Ross-Kerr, J. C., and Wood, M. J. (2006), pp. 419-420.

Day, R. A., Paul, P, Williams, B., Smeltzer, S. C., and Bare, B. (2007), p. 445.

69. CORRECT ANSWER: 3

1. Maintaining a high level of care at all times does not address the nurse's frustration.

2. Decreasing the amount of time spent with Mrs. Peters does not solve the nurse's problem of frustration and may not be beneficial to Mrs. Peters.

■ **3. Discussing the subject with another nurse might allow the nurse caring for Mrs. Peters to gain a deeper insight into her or his own feelings and further steps that need to be taken.**

4. This approach does not promote communication among staff who may not be aware of the problem. This also does not foster the nurse's professional growth.

CLASSIFICATION

COMPETENCY CATEGORY: Health and Wellness

TAXONOMIC LEVEL: Application

CLIENT TYPE: Individual

AGE GROUP: Adult of Advanced Age

REFERENCES

Arnold, E. C., and Underman Boggs, K. (2007), p. 94.

Canadian Nurses Association. (2008), pp. 8-9.

70. CORRECT ANSWER: **3**

1. Suctioning the oral cavity first would not clear the main air passage and may spread microorganisms.

2. Suctioning is necessary to clear the air passage; however, prolonged suctioning will decrease oxygen supply.

■ **3. Insertion without applying suction prevents trauma to the mucous membrane.**

4. Mrs. Peters should be placed in semi-Fowler's position as there is no indication that she is unconscious.

CLASSIFICATION

COMPETENCY CATEGORY: Changes in Health

TAXONOMIC LEVEL: Application

CLIENT TYPE: Individual

AGE GROUP: Adult of Advanced Age

REFERENCES

Day, R. A., Paul, P., Williams, B., Smeltzer, S. C., and Bare, B. (2007), p. 639.

Potter, P. A., Griffin Perry, A., Ross-Kerr, J. C., and Wood, M. J. (2006), p. 1108.

END OF CASE 15 RATIONALES

CASE 16 RATIONALES

71. CORRECT ANSWER: **2**

1. This is a good way for the nurse to prepare but will not generate interest among the students.

■ **2. Through these actions, the nurse is showing interest in the task to be performed. The nurse is also preparing to assume a leadership role with the students by encouraging their active participation from the outset.**

3. This will enable the nurse to make time for this new task in her or his work schedule but will do nothing to encourage student participation.

4. This will enable the nurse to gather documentation but will do nothing to encourage student participation.

CLASSIFICATION

COMPETENCY CATEGORY: Health and Wellness

TAXONOMIC LEVEL: Application

CLIENT TYPE: Group, Population, Community

AGE GROUP: Adolescent

REFERENCES

Craven, R. F., and Hirnle, C. J. (2009), pp. 17-22.

Nies, M. A., and McEwen, M. (2007), pp. 74-87.

72. CORRECT ANSWER: **4**

1. Students do not have any control over the number of physical education lessons in a week.

2. The physical exercise is determined by the nurse rather than the students; the students are not allowed to choose.

3. Students of this age have the ability to make choices. Peer influence is much more important than that of their parents. It is important first to speak with them and adopt a positive approach that focuses on strengths rather than on fear.

■ **4. An invitation issued to the students allows them to decide whether or not they wish to participate. Moreover, choosing activities they like and scheduling them during the lunch break takes into account the students' preferences and circumstances.**

CLASSIFICATION

COMPETENCY CATEGORY: Health and Wellness
TAXONOMIC LEVEL: Critical Thinking
CLIENT TYPE: Group, Population, Community
AGE GROUP: Adolescent

REFERENCES

Craven, R. F., and Hirnle, C. J. (2009), pp. 17-22.
Nies, M. A., and McEwen, M. (2007), pp. 85-91.

73. CORRECT ANSWER: **4**

1. This is an example of secondary prevention designed to get a group of students to slow down the disease process (obesity), thereby improving their condition.

2. This is a primary prevention activity designed to reduce the risk of this pathology developing in a group allegedly at risk.

3. This activity is an example of screening. It is a secondary prevention activity.

■ **4. This guide promotes healthy eating as a way of improving people's health. It is an example of health promotion.**

CLASSIFICATION

COMPETENCY CATEGORY: Health and Wellness
TAXONOMIC LEVEL: Application
CLIENT TYPE: Group, Population, Community
AGE GROUP: Adolescent

REFERENCES

Craven, R. F., and Hirnle, C. J. (2009), pp. 223-230.
Nies, M. A., and McEwen, M. (2007), pp. 614-615.

74. CORRECT ANSWER: **3**

1. This is not a principle of primary health care.

2. This is a principle of primary health care but not the one sought in this case.

■ **3. Stigmatization is one of the challenges associated with accessibility, which is a principle of primary health care.**

4. This is a population health determinant, not a principle of primary health care.

CLASSIFICATION

COMPETENCY CATEGORY: Health and Wellness
TAXONOMIC LEVEL: Application
CLIENT TYPE: Group, Population, Community
AGE GROUP: Adolescent

REFERENCES

Craven, R. F., and Hirnle, C. J. (2009), p. 16.
Nies, M. A., and McEwen, M. (2007), pp. 178-179.

75. CORRECT ANSWER: **2**

1. This action takes into account the nurse's perspective only and does not consider the group's development.

■ **2. This action shows that the nurse is working in a partnership arrangement and values the community partners' contribution to the process.**

3. This action shows no collaboration with the committee.

4. This action does not take into account the nurse's perspective and the group's development.

CLASSIFICATION

COMPETENCY CATEGORY: Professional Practice
TAXONOMIC LEVEL: Critical Thinking
CLIENT TYPE: Group, Population, Community
AGE GROUP: Adolescent

REFERENCES

Craven, R. F., and Hirnle, C. J. (2009), pp. 16-22.
Nies, M. A., and McEwen, M. (2007), p. 17.

76. CORRECT ANSWER: **1**

■ **1. This is an evaluation method that can be used to verify the students' satisfaction with activities. Facial expression is a non-verbal communication method.**

2. This method gathers information on the weight lost by students in the school but not on their satisfaction with the activities. This method assesses the effectiveness of activities, not the satisfaction of participants.

3. This method gathers information on the health committee's level of productivity, not on the students' satisfaction with the activities.

4. This method gathers information on the number of participants at the start of the activities but provides no information on their level of satisfaction.

CLASSIFICATION

COMPETENCY CATEGORY: Changes in Health
TAXONOMIC LEVEL: Critical Thinking
CLIENT TYPE: Group, Population, Community
AGE GROUP: Adolescent

REFERENCES

Nies, M. A., and McEwen, M. (2007), pp. 94-95.
Potter, P. A., Griffin Perry, A., Ross-Kerr, J. C., and Wood, M. J. (2006), pp. 184-186.

END OF CASE 16 RATIONALES

CASE 17 RATIONALES

77. CORRECT ANSWER: **3**

1. This may not be feasible and the nurse is not proactive in educating herself or himself.
2. This may not be feasible and is not the best option to increase knowledge.
■ 3. **This is the best option to increase knowledge, competence and nursing role.**
4. This does not address the issue of increasing the nurse's knowledge.

CLASSIFICATION

COMPETENCY CATEGORY: Professional Practice
TAXONOMIC LEVEL: Application
CLIENT TYPE: Individual
AGE GROUP: Young Adult

REFERENCES

Craven, R. F., and Hirnle, C. J. (2009), p. 198.
Potter, P. A., Griffin Perry, A., Ross-Kerr, J. C., and Wood, M. J. (2006), pp. 166-168.

78. CORRECT ANSWER: **3**

1. This information is part of a broad assessment and should not be done as a stand-alone assessment.
2. This is the initial visit, and there is no evidence that the client is suicidal.
■ 3. **It is at the initial visit that baseline data are collected and should include all activities of daily living and physical assessment.**
4. This information is not necessary at this time.

CLASSIFICATION

COMPETENCY CATEGORY: Changes in Health
TAXONOMIC LEVEL: Knowledge/Comprehension
CLIENT TYPE: Individual
AGE GROUP: Young Adult

REFERENCES

Mantik Lewis, S., McLean Heitkemper, M., Ruff Dirksen, S., Graber O'Brien, P., and Bucher, L. (2007), p. 255.
Taylor, C., Lillis, C., LeMone, P., and Lynn, P. (2008), pp. 241-248.

79. CORRECT ANSWER: **3**

1. This does not respect the client's request and may be judgmental on the part of the nurse.
2. This is a judgmental statement. The care should not be based on the nurse's values but the client's.
■ 3. **An awareness of values is essential to planning and delivering nursing care. This option respects everyone's concerns.**
4. This does not respect the family's wishes.

CLASSIFICATION

COMPETENCY CATEGORY: Nurse-Client Partnership
TAXONOMIC LEVEL: Critical Thinking
CLIENT TYPE: Family
AGE GROUP: Young Adult

REFERENCES

Arnold, E. C., and Underman Boggs, K. (2007), p. 45.
Taylor, C., Lillis, C., LeMone, P., and Lynn, P. (2008), pp. 99-100.

80. CORRECT ANSWER: 2

1. This does not allow for discussion or meeting psychosocial needs.

■ **2. This supports the family in their psychosocial needs by allowing them to discuss and work through issues.**

3. The nurse is making this decision and it is not appropriate at this time.

4. This is not the most appropriate action because there are other family members who need to be considered as well.

CLASSIFICATION

COMPETENCY CATEGORY: Nurse-Client Partnership

TAXONOMIC LEVEL: Application

CLIENT TYPE: Family

AGE GROUP: Young Adult

REFERENCES

Mantik Lewis, S., McLean Heitkemper, M., Ruff Dirksen, S., Graber O'Brien, P., and Bucher, L. (2007), p. 160.

Ferrell, B. R., and Coyle, N. (2006), pp. 554-555.

81. CORRECT ANSWER: 2

1. HIV/AIDS is not transmitted through casual contact.

■ **2. HIV/AIDS is not transmitted through casual contact. It is okay to eat with, hug or touch someone with HIV/AIDS.**

3. HIV/AIDS is not transmitted through casual contact.

4. There is no HIV/AIDS immunization available.

CLASSIFICATION

COMPETENCY CATEGORY: Health and Wellness

TAXONOMIC LEVEL: Application

CLIENT TYPE: Family

AGE GROUP: Young Adult

REFERENCES

Mantik Lewis, S., McLean Heitkemper, M., Ruff Dirksen, S., Graber O'Brien, P., and Bucher, L. (2007), p. 250.

Stanhope, M., and Lancaster, J. (2008), p. 492.

END OF CASE 17 RATIONALES

CASE 18 RATIONALES

82. CORRECT ANSWER: **1**

■ 1. **Appropriate nursing interventions for an unconscious client include talking with the client while providing nursing care, explaining procedures and identifying who is in the room.**

2. The nurse should not discuss Susan's condition by talking "over" her. The nurse should assume that Susan can hear all conversations in her presence.

3. There is no need to speak slowly or clearly to an unconscious client. It is inappropriate to use the family to pressure Susan to perform activities.

4. Hearing is the last sensation lost with unconscious clients. Tactile stimulation is also important, but not at the expense of auditory stimulation; hence, whispering is an inappropriate approach.

CLASSIFICATION

COMPETENCY CATEGORY: Changes in Health

TAXONOMIC LEVEL: Application

CLIENT TYPE: Family

AGE GROUP: Adolescent

REFERENCES

Riley, J. B. (2008), p. 137.

Arnold, E. C., and Underman Boggs, K. (2007), p. 105.

83. CORRECT ANSWER: **3**

1. Taping the hole contravenes principles of asepsis.

2. The high concentration of glucose in the amino acid solution stimulates high levels of insulin production. Removing the glucose source suddenly can precipitate a dangerous hypoglycemic reaction.

■ 3. **Infusing dextrose 10% is the most appropriate action because it temporarily replaces the glucose source while the nurse waits for the delivery of the new bag.**

4. The lipids would be an inappropriate replacement for the glucose, and it would be incorrect to increase the rate at which lipids are being infused without a physician's order.

CLASSIFICATION

COMPETENCY CATEGORY: Changes in Health

TAXONOMIC LEVEL: Application

CLIENT TYPE: Individual

AGE GROUP: Adolescent

REFERENCES

Day, R. A., Paul, P., Williams, B., Smeltzer, S. C., and Bare, B. (2007), p. 1011.

Mantik Lewis, S., McLean Heitkemper, M., Ruff Dirksen, S., Goldsworthy, S., and Barry, M. A. (2006), p. 998.

84. CORRECT ANSWER: **2**

1. Resting splints prevent contracture deformity (foot drop) but do not promote circulation.

■ 2. **Contracting and relaxing the leg muscles, even through passive means, promotes circulation in the lower extremities.**

3. Administering warm packs to the calves is not an effective or safe measure to promote circulation.

4. Elevating the foot of the client's bed decreases arterial flow.

CLASSIFICATION

COMPETENCY CATEGORY: Changes in Health

TAXONOMIC LEVEL: Application

CLIENT TYPE: Individual

AGE GROUP: Adolescent

REFERENCES

Potter, P. A., Griffin Perry, A., Ross-Kerr, J. C., and Wood, M. J. (2006), p. 1446.

Elkin, M. K., Griffin Perry, A., and Potter, P. A. (2007), p. 94.

85. CORRECT ANSWER: 2

1. Good lighting is essential to assess the oxygen status of an unconscious client; therefore, lights should not be dimmed.

■ **2. Wrinkle-free linen prevents skin breakdown, which is a risk for the unconscious client.**

3. A prone position is not safe practice for a spinal cord injured, unconscious client because of the risk of aspiration.

4. Although Susan is unconscious, her privacy should still be maintained during personal care.

CLASSIFICATION

COMPETENCY CATEGORY: Changes in Health
TAXONOMIC LEVEL: Application
CLIENT TYPE: Individual
AGE GROUP: Adolescent

REFERENCES

Potter, P. A., Griffin Perry, A., Ross-Kerr, J. C., and Wood, M. J. (2006), p. 1499.

Day, R. A., Paul, P., Williams, B., Smeltzer, S. C., and Bare, B. (2007), p. 1866.

86. CORRECT ANSWER: 2

1. Documenting this situation does not have any direct effect on promoting a safe practice environment.

■ **2. Advising the nurse-in-charge is the best approach to promote a safe practice environment. It notifies the nurse-in-charge of the changing conditions on the unit and also sets in motion a plan for getting more help.**

3. It would be inappropriate to leave the bedside of the unstable client for an extended period.

4. It would be inappropriate for the practical nurse to provide care for a client who is not stable.

CLASSIFICATION

COMPETENCY CATEGORY: Professional Practice
TAXONOMIC LEVEL: Critical Thinking
CLIENT TYPE: Group, Population, Community
AGE GROUP: Not applicable

REFERENCES

Canadian Nurses Association. (2008), p. 8.

Potter, P. A., Griffin Perry, A., Ross-Kerr, J. C., and Wood, M. J. (2006), p. 120.

END OF CASE 18 RATIONALES

CASE 19 RATIONALES

87. CORRECT ANSWER: 2

1. Obtaining a nursing history is important, but not initially because Mr. Ralph may be experiencing respiratory distress.

■ **2. Mr. Ralph is experiencing an anaphylactic reaction and may suddenly develop respiratory distress.**

3. The physician needs to be notified but not prior to assessing the airway.

4. These are important interventions, but not initially. Assessing airway and breathing is always the initial intervention.

CLASSIFICATION

COMPETENCY CATEGORY: Changes in Health
TAXONOMIC LEVEL: Critical Thinking
CLIENT TYPE: Individual
AGE GROUP: Middle Adult

REFERENCES

Day, R. A., Paul, P., Williams, B., Smeltzer, S. C., and Bare, B. (2007), pp. 2176-2177.

Mantik Lewis, S., McLean Heitkemper, M., Ruff Dirksen, S., Graber O'Brien, P., and Bucher, L. (2007), p. 1790.

88. CORRECT ANSWER: 1

■ 1. This is the appropriate dosage following calculations: amount ordered/amount on hand × 10 mL.

2. This is the wrong dosage.

3. This is the wrong dosage following calculations.

4. This is the wrong dosage.

CLASSIFICATION

COMPETENCY CATEGORY: Changes in Health

TAXONOMIC LEVEL: Application

CLIENT TYPE: Individual

AGE GROUP: Middle Adult

REFERENCES

Niblett, V. (2006), p. 96.

Craven, R. F., and Hirnle, C. J. (2009), p. 510.

89. CORRECT ANSWER: 1

■ 1. Common side effects of epinephrine (Adrenalin) are restlessness and tremors.

2. These symptoms are normal side effects of epinephrine (Adrenalin).

3. These symptoms are normal side effects of epinephrine (Adrenalin).

4. Documentation is important but these symptoms are normal side effects of epinephrine (Adrenalin).

CLASSIFICATION

COMPETENCY CATEGORY: Changes in Health

TAXONOMIC LEVEL: Critical Thinking

CLIENT TYPE: Family

AGE GROUP: Middle Adult

REFERENCES

Karch, A. M. (2008), p. 440.

Canadian Pharmacists Association (2008), p. 815.

90. CORRECT ANSWER: 1

■ 1. Having Mr. Ralph and his family demonstrate the use of the EpiPen ensures that they know how to use the pen appropriately.

2. If Mr. Ralph develops the signs and symptoms, he should administer the epinephrine (Adrenalin) and then proceed to the emergency department.

3. This is correct but the nurse must first ensure that the client and family know how to properly use the EpiPen.

4. This is important because the client does not have a history of allergies but this is not the most important teaching at this time.

 END OF CASE 19 RATIONALES

CLASSIFICATION

COMPETENCY CATEGORY: Changes in Health

TAXONOMIC LEVEL: Application

CLIENT TYPE: Family

AGE GROUP: Middle Adult

REFERENCES

Craven, R. F., and Hirnle, C. J. (2009), pp. 509-510.

Mantik Lewis, S., McLean Heitkemper, M., Ruff Dirksen, S., Graber O'Brien, P., and Bucher, L. (2007), p. 1790.

91. CORRECT ANSWER: 4

1. The wrong route is given.

2. The medication dose is correct.

3. Acetaminophen (Tylenol) is an antipyretic.

■ **4. Paul has a nasogastric tube in and the medication should be administered via another route.**

CLASSIFICATION

COMPETENCY CATEGORY: Changes in Health

TAXONOMIC LEVEL: Critical Thinking

CLIENT TYPE: Individual

AGE GROUP: Newborn and Infants

REFERENCES

Potter, P. A., Griffin Perry, A., Ross-Kerr, J. C., and Wood, M. J. (2006), p. 850.

Potter, P. A., and Griffin Perry, A. (2007), p. 618.

92. CORRECT ANSWER: 1

■ **1. After initial confirmation is done via X-ray, a pH strip is used for subsequent confirmation. A pH of five or less is accepted as indicating gastric content; if higher, another X-ray may be required.**

2. This is unreliable due to the similarity of sounds in bronchus, esophagus or pleural space.

3. After initial X-ray confirmation, pH can be used for subsequent testing if the pH is five or less. If greater than five, another X-ray may be required.

4. This may cause trauma.

CLASSIFICATION

COMPETENCY CATEGORY: Changes in Health

TAXONOMIC LEVEL: Knowledge/Comprehension

CLIENT TYPE: Individual

AGE GROUP: Newborn and Infants

REFERENCES

Hockenberry, M. J., and Wilson, D. (2007), pp. 1132-1133.

Potter, P. A., and Griffin Perry, A. (2007), p. 1021.

93. CORRECT ANSWER: 2

1. Although the nurse will do this, Paul's safety must be ensured first.

■ **2. This is the nurse's first priority. When the nasogastric tube is pulled, there is a risk of aspiration and trauma with the reinsertion.**

3. This does not address the fact that the nurse witnessed the mother pulling out the tube.

4. It is important to document findings but Paul's safety is a priority.

CLASSIFICATION

COMPETENCY CATEGORY: Professional Practice

TAXONOMIC LEVEL: Critical Thinking

CLIENT TYPE: Family

AGE GROUP: Newborn and Infants

REFERENCES

Hockenberry, M. J., and Wilson, D. (2007), p. 1420.

Potter, P. A., Griffin Perry, A., Ross-Kerr, J. C., and Wood, M. J. (2006), p. 58.

94. CORRECT ANSWER: 2

1. The underlying problem is respiratory status, not fatigue.

■ **2. The nurse is demonstrating accountability by recognizing limitations and seeking assistance.**

3. It is the nurse's responsibility to report episodic changes.

4. It is not appropriate for the nurse to transfer the assignment to another staff member.

CLASSIFICATION

COMPETENCY CATEGORY: Professional Practice

TAXONOMIC LEVEL: Critical Thinking

CLIENT TYPE: Individual

AGE GROUP: Newborn and Infants

REFERENCES

Canadian Nurses Association. (2008), p. 18.

Day, R. A., Paul, P., Williams, B., Smeltzer, S. C., and Bare, B. (2007), p. 28.

END OF CASE 20 RATIONALES

CASE 21 RATIONALES

95. CORRECT ANSWER: 2

1. Deep, rapid respirations occur to rid the body of excess acid.

■ **2. Fatigue is a component of the anemia that occurs because of decreased erythropoietin and is common in renal failure.**

3. Hypertension occurs because of increased fluid retention.

4. Warm, flushed skin is a component of the metabolic acidosis that occurs in chronic renal failure.

CLASSIFICATION

COMPETENCY CATEGORY: Changes in Health

TAXONOMIC LEVEL: Knowledge/Comprehension

CLIENT TYPE: Individual

AGE GROUP: Older Adult

REFERENCES

Mantik Lewis, S., McLean Heitkemper, M., Ruff Dirksen, S., Goldsworthy, S., and Barry, M. A. (2006), p. 1226.

Day, R. A., Paul, P., Williams, B., Smeltzer, S. C., and Bare, B. (2007), p. 1328.

96. CORRECT ANSWER: 3

1. His PCO_2 is normal, which indicates that he does not have a respiratory problem. The pH indicates acidosis.

2. His PCO_2 is normal, which indicates that he does not have a respiratory problem. The pH indicates acidosis.

■ **3. The pH indicates acidosis, and his HCO_3^- is below 22-26 mmol/L.**

4. The pH indicates acidosis, and his HCO_3^- is not elevated.

CLASSIFICATION

COMPETENCY CATEGORY: Changes in Health

TAXONOMIC LEVEL: Critical Thinking

CLIENT TYPE: Individual

AGE GROUP: Older Adult

REFERENCES

Day, R. A., Paul, P., Williams, B., Smeltzer, S. C., and Bare, B. (2007), p. 288.

Mantik Lewis, S., McLean Heitkemper, M., Ruff Dirksen, S., Goldsworthy, S., and Barry, M. A. (2006), pp. 356-357.

97. CORRECT ANSWER: **1**

- ■ 1. **Correct, based on calculation formula: drop rate = gtt factor/60 × flow rate/time.**

- 2. Incorrect, based on calculation formula: drop rate = gtt factor/60 × flow rate/time.

- 3. Incorrect, based on calculation formula: drop rate = gtt factor/60 × flow rate/time.

- 4. Incorrect, based on calculation formula: drop rate = gtt factor/60 × flow rate/time.

CLASSIFICATION

COMPETENCY CATEGORY: Changes in Health

TAXONOMIC LEVEL: Application

CLIENT TYPE: Individual

AGE GROUP: Older Adult

REFERENCES

Potter, P. A., Griffin Perry, A., Ross-Kerr, J. C., and Wood, M. J. (2006), p. 1187.

Taylor, C., Lillis, C., and LeMone, P. (2005), p. 1466.

98. CORRECT ANSWER: **4**

- 1. Fluids are restricted to prevent fluid overload. Protein should be reduced to prevent accumulation of toxic end products.

- 2. Fluids are restricted to prevent fluid overload. Protein should be reduced to prevent accumulation of toxic end products.

- 3. Calories from carbohydrates are needed to minimize catabolism of body protein. Fluids are restricted to prevent fluid overload.

- ■ 4. **Calories from carbohydrates are needed to minimize catabolism of body protein. Fluids are restricted to prevent fluid overload.**

CLASSIFICATION

COMPETENCY CATEGORY: Changes in Health

TAXONOMIC LEVEL: Application

CLIENT TYPE: Individual

AGE GROUP: Older Adult

REFERENCES

Day, R. A., Paul, P., Williams, B., Smeltzer, S. C., and Bare, B. (2007), p. 1330.

Mantik Lewis, S., McLean Heitkemper, M., Ruff Dirksen, S., Goldsworthy, S., and Barry, M. A. (2006), p. 1234.

99. CORRECT ANSWER: **1**

- ■ 1. **The first approach should be to involve the family in the plan of care before applying restraints.**

- 2. A least-restraint approach is recommended to ensure highest quality care. Restraints should be used as a last resort.

- 3. This will not prevent Mr. Brown from climbing out of bed.

- 4. Amount of medications should be minimized due to his impaired kidney function.

CLASSIFICATION

COMPETENCY CATEGORY: Professional Practice

TAXONOMIC LEVEL: Critical Thinking

CLIENT TYPE: Family

AGE GROUP: Older Adult

REFERENCES

Potter, P. A., Griffin Perry, A., Ross-Kerr, J. C., and Wood, M. J. (2006), pp. 992-993.

Ebersole, P., Hess, P., Touhy, T., Jett, K., and Luggen, A. (2008), pp. 381-383.

END OF CASE 21 RATIONALES

*RATIONALES 100 to 200 do **not** refer to a case.*

100. CORRECT ANSWER: 2

1. Beta blockers do not need to be withheld for this reason.

■ **2. Beta blockers are contraindicated in clients experiencing significant bradycardia.**

3. Persistent fatigue is common in clients who have recently experienced a myocardial infarction and is not a reason to withhold this medication.

4. Beta blockers do not need to be withheld for this reason.

CLASSIFICATION

COMPETENCY CATEGORY: Changes in Health

TAXONOMIC LEVEL: Critical Thinking

CLIENT TYPE: Individual

AGE GROUP: Middle Adult

REFERENCES

Lilley, L. L., Harrington, S., Snyder, J. S., and Swart, B. (2007), p. 310.

Lehne, R. A. (2007), p. 173.

101. CORRECT ANSWER: 1

■ **1. Daily weight monitoring is the most reliable indicator of volume status.**

2. Blood pressure decrease might indicate a change in volume or vasodilatation from other antihypertensive medications.

3. Urine output without a measure of intake does not reveal a change in volume status. It may be that intake was also increased.

4. This is not the best way to assess for volume status.

CLASSIFICATION

COMPETENCY CATEGORY: Changes in Health

TAXONOMIC LEVEL: Application

CLIENT TYPE: Individual

AGE GROUP: Older Adult

REFERENCES

Mantik Lewis, S., McLean Heitkemper, M., Ruff Dirksen, S., Goldsworthy, S., and Barry, M. A. (2006), p. 315.

Day, R. A., Paul, P., Williams, B., Smeltzer, S. C and Bare, B. (2007), p. 263.

102. CORRECT ANSWER: 3

1. James has rated his pain as moderate to severe. Clients can be resting as pain can cause fatigue. The nurse should administer an analgesic if ordered.

2. School-age children are able to accurately describe the intensity of their pain.

■ **3. James' report of pain should be accepted as the most reliable indicator of pain. He is able to assess the intensity of his pain and should be believed.**

4. James has rated the intensity of his pain and a visual analog scale is not required.

CLASSIFICATION

COMPETENCY CATEGORY: Professional Practice

TAXONOMIC LEVEL: Critical Thinking

CLIENT TYPE: Family

AGE GROUP: Older Child

REFERENCES

Mantik Lewis, S., McLean Heitkemper, M., Ruff Dirksen, S., Graber O'Brien, P., and Bucher, L. (2007), p. 142.

James, S. R., and Ashwill, J. W. (2007), p. 399.

103. CORRECT ANSWER: 3

1. The nurse would be breaching confidentiality and should never give access to information to another person.

2. The nurse would be breaching confidentiality by telling the co-worker private information about clients.

■ **3. The nurse should ensure confidentiality of client information.**

4. The nurse would be violating the client's confidentiality regardless of when the electronic health record was accessed.

CLASSIFICATION

COMPETENCY CATEGORY: Professional Practice

TAXONOMIC LEVEL: Application

CLIENT TYPE: Individual

AGE GROUP: Not applicable

REFERENCES

Potter, P. A., and Griffin Perry, A. (2007), pp. 146-147.

Potter, P. A., Griffin Perry, A., Ross-Kerr, J. C., and Wood, M. J. (2006), p. 116.

104. CORRECT ANSWER: 2

1. This is not the priority action.

■ **2. Standard protocol for nitroglycerin tablets is to repeat every five minutes up to three doses.**

3. Although Mr. Huber may need hospitalization, he must receive the nitroglycerin in order to maintain perfusion to the heart muscle. It would be more appropriate to call emergency services than to transport Mr. Huber personally.

4. Mr. Huber is in pain and the first action is to ensure that he takes the nitroglycerin.

CLASSIFICATION

COMPETENCY CATEGORY: Changes in Health

TAXONOMIC LEVEL: Critical Thinking

CLIENT TYPE: Individual

AGE GROUP: Middle Adult

REFERENCES

Brophy, K. M., Scarlett-Ferguson, H., and Webber, K. S. (2008), p. 872.

Day, R. A., Paul, P., Williams, B., Smeltzer, S. C., and Bare, B. (2007), p. 658.

105. CORRECT ANSWER: 4

1. Eating all the food on the tray indicates that Mr. Southworth has a good appetite and does not indicate readiness to learn.

2. This statement reflects a lack of knowledge and not readiness to learn.

3. Discussing a friend with diabetes indicates that Mr. Southworth may have some knowledge of diabetes on the basis of previous experience but does not indicate readiness to learn.

■ **4. One indication of his readiness to learn is when Mr. Southworth seeks out information by asking related questions.**

CLASSIFICATION

COMPETENCY CATEGORY: Nurse-Client Partnership

TAXONOMIC LEVEL: Application

CLIENT TYPE: Individual

AGE GROUP: Young Adult

REFERENCES

Potter, P. A., Griffin Perry, A., Ross-Kerr, J. C., and Wood, M. J. (2006), pp. 331-332.

Bastable, S. (2008), pp. 207-208.

106. CORRECT ANSWER: **2**

1. Inserting objects inside a cast should be discouraged because it could cause more injury to the extremity.

■ **2. Elevating a casted extremity prevents swelling and pain and promotes circulation.**

3. Injured bones and tissue are now stabilized; therefore, the client should not experience high levels of pain for such a long period.

4. The client should never use a hair dryer to dry wet plaster because plaster cracks and skin underneath could be damaged.

CLASSIFICATION

COMPETENCY CATEGORY: Changes in Health

TAXONOMIC LEVEL: Application

CLIENT TYPE: Individual

AGE GROUP: Adolescent

REFERENCES

Kuhn Timby, B., and Smith, N. E. (2007), p. 1193

Potter, P. A., Griffin Perry, A., Ross-Kerr, J. C., and Wood, M. J. (2006), p. 307.

107. CORRECT ANSWER: **3**

1. Providing praise is used in family communication to highlight the previous strengths and coping of the family.

2. This is part of the initial phase of group process when the group is forming and developing trust.

■ **3. This is referred to as the storming phase. It signals an important phase in group process as the group is challenging the status quo and developing group norms.**

4. This may help with the initial forming of the group but is not an appropriate strategy for facilitating the work of the group.

CLASSIFICATION

COMPETENCY CATEGORY: Nurse-Client Partnershi

TAXONOMIC LEVEL: Application

CLIENT TYPE: Group, Population, Community

AGE GROUP: Not applicable

REFERENCES

Arnold, E. C., and Underman Boggs, K. (2007) pp. 275-278, 310.

Marquis, B. L., and Huston, C. J. (2009), pp. 456-457.

108. CORRECT ANSWER: **1**

■ **1. This practice is outside the nurse's roles and responsibilities, and this point needs to be articulated.**

2. This procedure is outside the nurse's scope of practice whether or not the physician is present.

3. This procedure is outside the nurse's scope of practice.

4. This procedure is outside the nurse's scope of practice.

CLASSIFICATION

COMPETENCY CATEGORY: Professional Practice

TAXONOMIC LEVEL: Application

CLIENT TYPE: Individual

AGE GROUP: Not applicable

REFERENCES

Potter, P. A., Griffin Perry, A., Ross-Kerr, J. C., and Wood, M. J. (2006), pp. 1661-1662.

Donovan Monahan, F., Sands, J. K., Neighbors, M., Marek, J. F., and Green-Nigro, C. J. (2007), p. 1.

109. CORRECT ANSWER: 4

1. It is safe to resume sex 7 to 10 days after an uncomplicated myocardial infarction.

2. The physician will determine when Mrs. King can return to work on the basis of how she feels.

3. Walking should start at 10 minutes per day and be increased gradually.

■ **4. This monitors Mrs. King in the early phase of recovery and provides continuity of care.**

CLASSIFICATION

COMPETENCY CATEGORY: Health and Wellness

TAXONOMIC LEVEL: Knowledge/Comprehension

CLIENT TYPE: Individual

AGE GROUP: Middle Adult

REFERENCES

Mantik Lewis, S., McLean Heitkemper, M., Ruff Dirksen, S., Goldsworthy, S., and Barry, M. A. (2006), pp. 840-843.

Day, R. A., Paul, P., Williams, B., Smeltzer, S. C., and Bare, B. (2007), p. 738.

110. CORRECT ANSWER: 2

1. This site is not preferred for children because it is not well developed.

■ **2. Research has shown that the dorsogluteal site is no longer recommended for IM injections. The ventrogluteal site is less painful and free of major blood vessels and is recommended for children over 7 years of age to adults.**

3. The landmarking for the ventrogluteal ensures a safer site. This site is also free of major blood vessels and nerves. Ventrogluteal is the preferred site in children over 7 years of age.

4. The dorsogluteal site is not recommended as an injection site. Research has shown that this site may result in complications and should no longer be used.

CLASSIFICATION

COMPETENCY CATEGORY: Professional Practice

TAXONOMIC LEVEL: Application

CLIENT TYPE: Individual

AGE GROUP: Older Child

REFERENCES

Hockenberry, M. J. (2005), p. 754.

Potter, P. A., Griffin Perry, A., Ross-Kerr, J. C., and Wood, M. J. (2006), p. 897.

111. CORRECT ANSWER: 2

1. Although daily walks may help Mr. Picquot, the nurse should not tell him what to do but rather should explore options with him.

■ **2. Mr. Picquot's subjective history indicates that he is having trouble coping. The nurse should explore support groups with Mr. Picquot.**

3. This solution does not deal with the underlying cause and takes responsibility from Mr. Picquot.

4. Although a massage therapist may be beneficial, the nurse is deciding what is best for Mr. Picquot. Coping strategies depend on individual needs.

CLASSIFICATION

COMPETENCY CATEGORY: Health and Wellness

TAXONOMIC LEVEL: Application

CLIENT TYPE: Individual

AGE GROUP: Adult of Advanced Age

REFERENCES

Miller, C. A. (2009), p. 206.

Potter, P. A., Griffin Perry, A., Ross-Kerr, J. C., and Wood, M. J. (2006), pp. 10, 449-450, 543.

112. CORRECT ANSWER: 4

1. The nurse should approach the colleague first before speaking with anyone else.

2. This will not address the issue of conflict of interest.

3. The nurse should approach the colleague first before speaking with anyone else.

■ 4. **The nurse should approach the colleague first before speaking with anyone else.**

CLASSIFICATION

COMPETENCY CATEGORY: Nurse-Client Partnership

TAXONOMIC LEVEL: Application

CLIENT TYPE: Individual

AGE GROUP: Not applicable

REFERENCES

Potter, P. A., Griffin Perry, A. G., Ross-Kerr, J. C. and Wood, M. J. (2006), p. 29.

Canadian Nurses Association. (2004), p. 47.

113. CORRECT ANSWER: 4

1. This involves entering the client's personal space. It would be safest to assess the client's level of agitation before conducting the assessment in order to reduce risk of injury to the nurse.

2. This is contraindicated in persons with dementia because too much information may increase their anxiety and agitation.

3. This may be appropriate after the client's level of agitation is assessed, but it may increase the level of agitation unnecessarily.

■ 4. **This is appropriate to decrease the environmental stimuli. It offers choices and allows time for transitioning to reduce the risk of anxiety and aggression.**

CLASSIFICATION

COMPETENCY CATEGORY: Changes in Health

TAXONOMIC LEVEL: Critical Thinking

CLIENT TYPE: Individual

AGE GROUP: Adult of Advanced Age

REFERENCES

Austin, W., and Boyd, M. A. (2008), pp. 732, 84?

Stuart, G. W., and Laraia, M. T. (2005), p. 467.

114. CORRECT ANSWER: 2

1. The length of shift remaining is not relevant if the nurse cannot manage the care alone.

■ 2. **The nurse must prioritize client needs.**

3. Administrative tasks do not take priority over the nursing care needs of clients.

4. No matter how experienced, the practical nurse cannot carry out the full range of nursing responsibilities.

CLASSIFICATION

COMPETENCY CATEGORY: Professional Practice

TAXONOMIC LEVEL: Application

CLIENT TYPE: Group, Population, Community

AGE GROUP: Not applicable

REFERENCES

Potter, P. A., Griffin Perry, A., Ross-Kerr, J. C., and Wood, M. J. (2006), p. 245.

Canadian Nurses Association. (2008), pp. 8-9

115. CORRECT ANSWER: 3

1. Although the client may need encouragement to breathe on his own, most likely after numerous attempts, this is not the main problem.

2. Although this may be a possibility, without knowing what the reason is, it may stall the problem of not being able to discontinue full mechanical assistance.

■ **3. Unless the client is unresponsive, he is in the best position to know his needs. Pain or fatigue may be factors contributing to unsuccessful weaning and are often best known by the client.**

4. While anxiolytics may provide comfort to the client, they could depress the respiratory system and will not necessarily contribute to weaning.

CLASSIFICATION

COMPETENCY CATEGORY: Changes in Health

TAXONOMIC LEVEL: Critical Thinking

CLIENT TYPE: Individual

AGE GROUP: Middle Adult

REFERENCES

Arnold, E. C., and Underman Boggs, K. (2007), p. 155.

Black, J. M., and Hokanson Hawks, J. (2009), p. 1652.

116. CORRECT ANSWER: 3

1. This does not address the client's needs.

2. This assumes that going to bed late is the problem.

■ **3. This is a relaxation technique that may aid in sleep and decrease stress.**

4. This is not practical. While beneficial, the client may not have the resources.

CLASSIFICATION

COMPETENCY CATEGORY: Health and Wellness

TAXONOMIC LEVEL: Application

CLIENT TYPE: Individual

AGE GROUP: Middle Adult

REFERENCES

Potter, P. A., Griffin Perry, A., Ross-Kerr, J. C., and Wood, M. J. (2006), p. 555.

Potter, P. A., and Griffin Perry, A. (2007), pp. 829-830.

117. CORRECT ANSWER: 3

1. This is not appropriate as Ms. Shetland's boyfriend is not the client.

2. In no case is violence acceptable. The nurse needs to assess whether the client and the nurse are at risk for harm.

■ **3. Assessment is the priority.**

4. This is impractical because there is no way to be sure that Ms. Shetland's boyfriend will be absent.

CLASSIFICATION

COMPETENCY CATEGORY: Health and Wellness

TAXONOMIC LEVEL: Critical Thinking

CLIENT TYPE: Family

AGE GROUP: Young Adult

REFERENCES

Arnold, E. C., and Underman Boggs, K. (2007), p. 336.

Nies, M. A., and McEwen, M. (2007), p. 306.

118. CORRECT ANSWER: 2

1. Evelyn is exhibiting manifestations of asthma, not a viral infection.

■ **2. These are potential signs of asthma exacerbation; respiratory status needs to be determined.**

3. Cold air will cause exacerbation.

4. Asthma can lead to fatigue; however, fatigue would not cause exacerbation.

CLASSIFICATION

COMPETENCY CATEGORY: Changes in Health

TAXONOMIC LEVEL: Knowledge/Comprehension

CLIENT TYPE: Individual

AGE GROUP: Older Child

REFERENCES

Smeltzer, S. C., Bare, B., Hinkle, J. L., and Cheever, K. H. (2007), pp. 591-596.

Hockenberry, M. J., and Wilson, D. (2009), p. 1450.

119. CORRECT ANSWER: 1

■ **1. This is an effective strategy to teach about aspects of family planning because the members of the group are familiar with each other. Group members who are more willing to participate can have the effect of drawing more hesitant members into active participation. In addition, this type of competition is appropriate for this age group.**

2. This will allow some presentation of knowledge on topics, but not active participation.

3. This will reinforce the knowledge presented, but it does not allow for active participation.

4. This will enable the group members to assess their knowledge on the topics and allow for individual members to participate, but it does not allow for active participation of the group.

CLASSIFICATION

COMPETENCY CATEGORY: Nurse-Client Partnership

TAXONOMIC LEVEL: Application

CLIENT TYPE: Group, Population, Community

AGE GROUP: Adolescents

REFERENCES

Kyle, T. (2008), pp. 58-63.

Bastable, S. (2008), pp. 170-171.

120. CORRECT ANSWER: 3

1. This is not appropriate because she has a patient-controlled analgesia (PCA) pump. All other pain medications should be on hold.

2. This is not the initial nursing action. The nurse would want to ensure that the client is using the PCA pump effectively.

■ **3. This maintains the principles of PCA and provides opportunity for reinforcement of how the pump works.**

4. This needs to be the nurse's decision, not the client's. All other pain medications should be on hold.

CLASSIFICATION

COMPETENCY CATEGORY: Changes in Health

TAXONOMIC LEVEL: Critical Thinking

CLIENT TYPE: Individual

AGE GROUP: Middle Adult

REFERENCES

Griffin Perry, A., and Potter, P. A. (2006), p. 141.

Black, J. M., and Hokanson Hawks, J. (2009), pp. 222-223, 375.

121. CORRECT ANSWER: 1

■ 1. **The nurse needs to conduct an assessment of the group prior to doing any teaching.**

2. This is not an initial action; the nurse needs to assess the needs of the group first.

3. This is a breach of confidentiality and may not be required.

4. Infant care and feeding are important, but this is not the initial action. An assessment needs to be completed first.

CLASSIFICATION

COMPETENCY CATEGORY: Nurse-Client Partnership

TAXONOMIC LEVEL: Application

CLIENT TYPE: Group, Population, Community

AGE GROUP: Adolescent

REFERENCES

Taylor, C., Lillis, C., LeMone, P., and Lynn, P. (2008), p. 510.

Wong, D. L., Perry, S. E., Hockenberry, M. J., Lowdermilk, D. L., and Wilson, D. (2006), pp. 1192-1193.

122. CORRECT ANSWER: 1

■ 1. **Oxygen therapy increases arterial oxygen saturation and increases the delivery of oxygen to the myocardium.**

2. Obtaining an electrocardiogram is critical to identifying acute changes in the case of an acute myocardial infarction (MI), but it is not the immediate intervention.

3. It is important to have a pain rating to base interventions on, but this is not the first intervention.

4. Sublingual nitroglycerin is part of the treatment protocol for an acute MI, but it is not the nurse's first action.

CLASSIFICATION

COMPETENCY CATEGORY: Changes in Health

TAXONOMIC LEVEL: Critical Thinking

CLIENT TYPE: Individual

AGE GROUP: Middle Adult

REFERENCES

Emergency Nurses Association. (2005). pp. 338-343.

Lehne, R. A. (2007), pp. 610-611.

123. CORRECT ANSWER: 3

1. The nurse requires protection.

2. This does not address the issue of the wet gown and mask not protecting the nurse.

■ 3. **A wet gown and mask no longer protect the nurse; therefore, the nurse must remove the wet gown and mask and apply new ones.**

4. This does not provide continuity of care.

CLASSIFICATION

COMPETENCY CATEGORY: Changes in Health

TAXONOMIC LEVEL: Application

CLIENT TYPE: Individual

AGE GROUP: Adolescent

REFERENCES

Potter, P. A., Griffin Perry, A., Ross-Kerr, J. C., and Wood, M. J. (2006), p. 809.

Potter, P. A., and Griffin Perry, A. (2007), p. 201.

124. CORRECT ANSWER: 4

1. People engage in this self-harm behaviour in an effort to affirm their reality and relieve tension rather than expressing a wish to die. Self-injury and suicidal behaviour are two separate phenomena.

2. People engage in this self-harm behaviour in an effort to affirm their reality, relieve tension, communicate distress or self-soothe with the release of endorphins.

3. This does not demonstrate the common reasons given for self-harm behaviour. Hallucinations are features of psychotic disorders. People with psychotic illness may harm themselves as a result of command hallucinations but it is not usually this sort of persistent self-mutilating behaviour. Moreover, there is nothing to suggest this client has a psychotic illness.

■ **4. People engage in this self-harm behaviour in an effort to affirm their reality, relieve tension, communicate distress or self-soothe with the release of endorphins.**

CLASSIFICATION

COMPETENCY CATEGORY: Professional Practice
TAXONOMIC LEVEL: Knowledge/Comprehension
CLIENT TYPE: Individual
AGE GROUP: Young Adult

REFERENCES

Ren Kneisl, C., and Trigoboff, E. (2009), p. 587.
Stuart, G. W., and Laraia, M. T. (2005), p. 367.

125. CORRECT ANSWER: 1

■ **1. Balancing the cardiac oxygen supply and the oxygen demand is priority for the client with an acute myocardial infarction.**

2. The nurse needs to apply oxygen first and then report assessment findings to the physician.

3. Slow, deep breathing will not alleviate shortness of breath and could, in fact, exacerbate it.

4. Diaphoresis is not necessarily related to increased temperature; oxygen will reduce the client's anxiety.

CLASSIFICATION

COMPETENCY CATEGORY: Changes in Health
TAXONOMIC LEVEL: Critical Thinking
CLIENT TYPE: Individual
AGE GROUP: Middle Adult

REFERENCES

Black, J. M., and Hokanson Hawks, J. (2009), pp. 1335, 1358.
Timby, B. K., and Smith, N. E. (2007), p. 477.

126. CORRECT ANSWER: 4

1. This may cause problems with liability and may spread the virus rather than contain it.

2. With a viral outbreak, clients should not be transferred to another facility as cross-contamination can occur.

3. Hand sanitizers will not help with the current staffing issue.

■ **4. Clients need to be attended to. It is important that these service providers do not have symptoms and use proper handwashing.**

CLASSIFICATION

COMPETENCY CATEGORY: Health and Wellness
TAXONOMIC LEVEL: Critical Thinking
CLIENT TYPE: Group, Population, Community
AGE GROUP: Not applicable

REFERENCES

Public Health Agency of Canada. (2005).
Ignatavicius, D. D., and Workman, M. L. (2006) pp. 1343-1344.

127. CORRECT ANSWER: 4

1. Megan is not fully conscious; therefore, this is a choking hazard.
2. If in doubt about blood sugar values, the nurse should treat for hypoglycemia.
3. Megan is not fully conscious; therefore, this is a choking hazard.
■ 4. **Because it is not known whether Megan is hypoglycemic or hyperglycemic, it is best to treat for hypoglycemia first.**

CLASSIFICATION

COMPETENCY CATEGORY: Changes in Health
TAXONOMIC LEVEL: Critical Thinking
CLIENT TYPE: Individual
AGE GROUP: Young Child

REFERENCES

Hockenberry, M. J., and Wilson, D. (2007), p. 1714.
Pillitteri, A. (2007), p. 1532.

128. CORRECT ANSWER: 3

1. Everyone is at risk of developing an alcohol problem.
2. Many people grow up in an environment in which there is alcohol use but never develop an alcohol-abuse problem.
■ 3. **Studies have established a link between sociocultural attitudes and alcohol abuse.**
4. The link between alcohol abuse and personality disorders has not been scientifically demonstrated.

CLASSIFICATION

COMPETENCY CATEGORY: Health and Wellness
TAXONOMIC LEVEL: Knowledge/Comprehension
CLIENT TYPE: Family
AGE GROUP: Adolescent

REFERENCES

Hockenberry, M. J., and Wilson, D. (2009), p. 91.
Allender, J. A., and Walton Spradley, B. (2005), p. 847.

129. CORRECT ANSWER: 4

1. This reaction is similar to denial in that it does not show personal awareness. If the nurse denies her feelings she will be less aware of the actions she takes.
2. This reaction may be premature. The nurse should attempt to deal with her feelings. The nurse should talk to a colleague who can help her become aware of what she is feeling and make the appropriate choices. The nurse may not be able to change assignments.
3. The client is not responsible for the nurse's feelings and must not be burdened with this problem.
■ 4. **Talking to a colleague can help the nurse become aware of what she is feeling and make the appropriate choices.**

CLASSIFICATION

COMPETENCY CATEGORY: Nurse-Client Partnership
TAXONOMIC LEVEL: Application
CLIENT TYPE: Individual
AGE GROUP: Not applicable

REFERENCES

Canadian Nurses Association. (2008), pp. 15-16.
Potter, P. A., and Griffin Perry, A. (2009), pp. 315, 353.

130. CORRECT ANSWER: 2

1. This is never a normal finding, although decelerations are more common after rupture of membranes and can correct themselves.

■ **2. This can indicate a prolapsed cord. One of the required interventions is to put the client in Trendelenburg, or from supine to lateral position, to relieve pressure on the cord if variable decelerations are severe.**

3. Early decelerations are due to head compressors.

4. This describes late decelerations.

CLASSIFICATION

COMPETENCY CATEGORY: Professional Practice
TAXONOMIC LEVEL: Critical Thinking
CLIENT TYPE: Individual
AGE GROUP: Middle Adult

REFERENCES

Leonard Lowdermilk, D., and Perry, E. S. (2007), pp. 506-507.

Wong, D. L., Perry, S. E., Hockenberry, M. J., Lowdermilk, D. L., and Wilson, D. (2006), pp. 474-475.

131. CORRECT ANSWER: 1

■ **1. Obsessive compulsive disorder (OCD) is an anxiety disorder and the ritual serves to control anxiety. Interfering with the ritual causes anxiety to escalate and can even precipitate panic. The team may eventually make a plan that involves asking the client to resist the ritual (response prevention), but it is premature for the intervention because the client has just been admitted.**

2. This is the same as interfering with the ritual.

3. Most clients with OCD understand that the ritual is not normal or necessary but are compelled to do it to control anxiety. The client has insight. The nurse should not attempt to reason or explain the client out of the behaviour.

4. Most clients with OCD understand that the ritual is not normal or necessary but are compelled to do it to control anxiety. The client has insight. The nurse should not attempt to reason or explain the client out of the behaviour.

CLASSIFICATION

COMPETENCY CATEGORY: Professional Practice
TAXONOMIC LEVEL: Critical Thinking
CLIENT TYPE: Individual
AGE GROUP: Middle Adult

REFERENCES

Ren Kneisl, C., and Trigoboff, E. (2009), p. 460.

Stuart, G. W., and Laraia, M. T. (2005), pp. 276-277.

132. CORRECT ANSWER: 3

1. This causes confusion and blurs nurse-client boundaries for the client.

2. Mr. Simpson cannot understand the logic behind the delusion and cannot be expected to explain it.

■ **3. This helps Mr. Simpson use his time constructively (e.g., physical activity).**

4. Delusions are fixed, false beliefs, and trying to argue their existence reasonably is not effective or therapeutic.

CLASSIFICATION

COMPETENCY CATEGORY: Health and Wellness
TAXONOMIC LEVEL: Application
CLIENT TYPE: Individual
AGE GROUP: Middle Adult

REFERENCES

Stuart, G. W., and Laraia, M. T. (2005), pp. 407-409.

Austin, W., and Boyd, M. A. (2008), pp. 350-351.

133. CORRECT ANSWER: 4

1. Epilepsy Canada recommends not putting objects into the mouth during a seizure.

2. Proper position is side-lying; there is increased risk of aspiration from vomitus when clients are placed on their back.

3. This would put the client at risk for musculoskeletal injury. Clothing should be loosened so as not to restrain Kassie.

■ **4. This protects Kassie from a traumatic injury.**

CLASSIFICATION

COMPETENCY CATEGORY: Health and Wellness

TAXONOMIC LEVEL: Application

CLIENT TYPE: Family

AGE GROUP: Young Child

REFERENCES

Potter, P. A., Griffin Perry, A., Ross-Kerr, J. C., and Wood, M. J. (2006), pp. 1003-1004.

Wong, D. L., Perry, S. E., Hockenberry, M. J., Lowdermilk, D. L., and Wilson, D. (2006), p. 1709.

134. CORRECT ANSWER: 2

1. The nurse should not assume that the problem is with medication. Failure to take medications is a common reason for psychotic symptoms to reoccur, but it is not always the reason.

■ **2. It is essential to listen to Mrs. Stonehouse and get information from her about her experience and to ask what she wants from the service provider. This is part of the initial phase of data gathering.**

3. Failure to take medications is a common reason for relapse of illness but it is not always the only reason, and this client may have problems in living rather than a relapse.

4. Hospitalization may not be necessary; assessment is required before considering any intervention.

CLASSIFICATION

COMPETENCY CATEGORY: Changes in Health

TAXONOMIC LEVEL: Application

CLIENT TYPE: Individual

AGE GROUP: Middle Adult

REFERENCES

Ren Kneisl, C., and Trigoboff, E. (2009), p. 216.

Austin, W., and Boyd, M. A. (2008), p. 152.

135. CORRECT ANSWER: 1

■ **1. Interprofessional team conferences enable sharing of information and joint decision-making from which comprehensive care plans can be developed and reviewed.**

2. Identification of discipline-specific health needs is the responsibility of the particular discipline.

3. Client care can easily become fragmented when health-care team members communicate between themselves on an individual basis only and not within the team.

4. The nurse is not responsible for making decisions for all health-care team members. This does not allow for joint decision-making.

CLASSIFICATION

COMPETENCY CATEGORY: Health and Wellness

TAXONOMIC LEVEL: Application

CLIENT TYPE: Individual

AGE GROUP: Not applicable

REFERENCES

Yoder-Wise, P. S. (2007), p. 251.

Potter, P. A., and Griffin Perry, A. (2007), pp. 119, 137.

136. CORRECT ANSWER: 3

1. This is partially correct but does not necessarily incorporate self-awareness of biases, prejudices and assumptions.

2. This is partially correct, but learning phrases in another language does not ensure cultural competence.

■ **3.** **This creates self-awareness of biases, prejudices and assumptions.**

4. This is unrealistic and does not necessarily lead to personal development and increased self-awareness.

CLASSIFICATION

COMPETENCY CATEGORY: Nurse-Client Partnership

TAXONOMIC LEVEL: Knowledge/Comprehension

CLIENT TYPE: Group, Population, Community

AGE GROUP: Not applicable

REFERENCES

Potter, P. A., Griffin Perry, A., Ross-Kerr, J. C., and Wood, M. J. (2006), p. 133.

Wilkinson, J. M., and Van Leuven, K. (2007), p. 235.

137. CORRECT ANSWER: 4

1. Although antibiotic use is a contributing factor, prescription is a medical decision.

2. This is important but it does not address the risk of contracting *Clostridium difficile*.

3. Isolation protocols are the nurse/staff's responsibility. It may also be difficult to identify those infected.

■ **4.** ***Clostridium difficile* is spread via fecal-oral route, and consistent handwashing is the best way to reduce infection.**

CLASSIFICATION

COMPETENCY CATEGORY: Health and Wellness

TAXONOMIC LEVEL: Knowledge/Comprehension

CLIENT TYPE: Individual

AGE GROUP: Adult of Advanced Age

REFERENCES

Meiner, S. E., and Lueckenotte, A. G. (2006), p. 336.

Zator Estes, M. E. (2008), p. 239.

138. CORRECT ANSWER: 2

1. Feedback that is emotional or judgmental is not constructive. Verbal feedback needs to be descriptive, specific and well-timed.

■ **2.** **The group's non-verbal behaviour will provide immediate feedback to the nurse. The expression of concrete and honest reactions that are based on observation of the group's behaviours provides an external view of how a person appears to others.**

3. This action would provide feedback from the group but would not be useful as a means of gathering initial feedback.

4. This action would provide feedback from the group but would not be useful as a means of gathering initial feedback.

CLASSIFICATION

COMPETENCY CATEGORY: Health and Wellness

TAXONOMIC LEVEL: Application

CLIENT TYPE: Group, Population, Community

AGE GROUP: Not applicable

REFERENCES

Arnold, E. C., and Underman Boggs, K. (2007), pp. 374-375.

Maurer, F. A., and Smith, C. (2009), p. 520.

139. CORRECT ANSWER: 1

- **1. Angiotensin II causes vasoconstriction and aldosterone retention, which increases blood volume. Angiotensin receptor blockers (ARBs) block angiotensin II action at receptor sites, resulting in vasodilation and a decrease in aldosterone (decreases sodium and water retention, which reduces blood volume).**

2. Angiotensin II causes vasoconstriction and aldosterone retention, which increases blood volume. ARBs block angiotensin II action at receptor sites, resulting in vasodilation and a decrease in aldosterone (decreases sodium and water retention, which reduces blood volume).

3. ARBs are vasodilators.

4. ARBs are vasodilators.

CLASSIFICATION

COMPETENCY CATEGORY: Changes in Health
TAXONOMIC LEVEL: Knowledge/Comprehension
CLIENT TYPE: Individual
AGE GROUP: Not applicable

REFERENCES

Abrams, A. C., Pennington, S. S., and Lammon, B. (2007), p. 842.

Lilley, L. L., Harrington, S., Snyder, J. S., and Swart, B. (2007), p. 407.

140. CORRECT ANSWER: 2

1. Anorexia nervosa is complex and cannot be explained so simply. It is premature for the nurse to assume knowledge of this client or her family, and it is never acceptable to attribute cause.

- **2. It is a priority that the client consumes a healthy amount of food. Involving the client in her own treatment planning gives her control and structure and promotes self-determination. Input into the plan fosters adherence. Validating the fear reassures the client that fears are not unique and shows respect for her experience.**

3. This fails to include the client in her own care and is not collaborative.

4. The nurse takes the lead in the discussion and makes judgmental assumptions rather than learning about and exploring Lydia's experience. Although power struggles are common, advice is not acceptable and would be damaging to the nurse-client relationship. It is not respectful and places the nurse in a parent position and Lydia in a child position.

CLASSIFICATION

COMPETENCY CATEGORY: Changes in Health
TAXONOMIC LEVEL: Application
CLIENT TYPE: Individual
AGE GROUP: Adolescent

REFERENCES

Ren Kneisl, C., and Trigoboff, E. (2009), pp. 560-563.

Austin, W., and Boyd, M. A. (2008), p. 481.

141. CORRECT ANSWER: 4

1. Although suicide represents a health risk, research has shown this is not the greatest health risk for this age group.

2. Although substance abuse represents a health risk, research has shown this is not the greatest health risk for this age group.

3. Although eating disorders represent a health risk, research has shown this is not the greatest health risk for this age group.

■ **4. Research has shown that unintentional injuries (e.g., from motor vehicle collisions) are still the leading health risk for youths.**

CLASSIFICATION

COMPETENCY CATEGORY: Health and Wellness
TAXONOMIC LEVEL: Knowledge/Comprehension
CLIENT TYPE: Group, Population, Community
AGE GROUP: Adolescent

REFERENCES

James, S. R., and Ashwill, J. W. (2007), p. 199.
Hockenberry, M. J., and Wilson, D. (2009), p. 538
Stanhope, M., and Lancaster, J. (2008), pp. 299-300.

142. CORRECT ANSWER: 2

1. Indiscriminate use of herbs may be unsafe; some herbs interact with certain drugs or may cause adverse effects in clients with cardiovascular disorders.

■ **2. This ensures that Mrs. Jacobsen's herbs are not contraindicated in relation to her diagnoses and/or medications.**

3. This does not support Mrs. Jacobsen's choice to use complementary medicines.

4. This does not support Mrs. Jacobsen's choice to use complementary medicines.

CLASSIFICATION

COMPETENCY CATEGORY: Health and Wellness
TAXONOMIC LEVEL: Application
CLIENT TYPE: Individual
AGE GROUP: Middle Adult

REFERENCES

Lilley, L. L., Harrington, S., Snyder, J. S., and Swart, B. (2007), p. 81.
Mantik Lewis, S., McLean Heitkemper, M., Ruff Dirksen, S., Goldsworthy, S., and Barry, M. A. (2006), p. 107.

143. CORRECT ANSWER: 3

1. The Glasgow coma scale is used to determine the level of consciousness.

2. Neurovascular assessment is not used to predict risk for skin breakdown.

■ **3. Risk assessment for skin breakdown should be done using a validated assessment tool such as the Braden scale.**

4. The CAGE questionnaire is used as a screening tool for alcohol consumption.

CLASSIFICATION

COMPETENCY CATEGORY: Health and Wellness
TAXONOMIC LEVEL: Knowledge/Comprehension
CLIENT TYPE: Individual
AGE GROUP: Adult of Advanced Age

REFERENCES

Mantik Lewis, S., McLean Heitkemper, M., Ruff Dirksen, S., Goldsworthy, S., and Barry, M. A. (2006), p. 229.
Potter, P. A., Griffin Perry, A., Ross-Kerr, J. C., and Wood, M. J. (2006), p. 1510.

144. CORRECT ANSWER: 4

1. Watching the child prepare all his medications puts unreasonably high expectations and responsibility on a 5-year-old child.

2. Telling the child to describe to his mother the pathology of cystic fibrosis is inappropriate; it is unreasonable to expect a 5-year-old child to understand and explain the pathology of a disease.

3. Asking the child if he understands everything that has been taught is not effective in getting him to demonstrate whether learning has occurred. The nurse should use an open-ended means of communication.

■ **4. Asking the child to point out different areas for chest physiotherapy on a doll allows him to recall basic facts and to use something tangible and familiar to demonstrate his knowledge. The nurse must consider the growth and development level of the child.**

CLASSIFICATION

COMPETENCY CATEGORY: Changes in Health
TAXONOMIC LEVEL: Critical Thinking
CLIENT TYPE: Individual
AGE GROUP: Young Child

REFERENCES

Potter, P. A., Griffin Perry, A., Ross-Kerr, J. C., and Wood, M. J. (2006), p. 322.
Pillitteri, A. (2007), p. 1051.

145. CORRECT ANSWER: 2

1. The nurse should avoid arguing, disputing or using logic to change the false beliefs.

■ **2. The nurse should respond to the underlying feelings. This answer is also a response to the real part of the communication.**

3. This does not validate the feeling of being alone, and it is premature to try to solve that problem without further discussion.

4. The nurse should not do anything to indicate to the client that she or he shares the false beliefs. Playing into the false belief is neither respectful nor therapeutic.

CLASSIFICATION

COMPETENCY CATEGORY: Changes in Health
TAXONOMIC LEVEL: Critical Thinking
CLIENT TYPE: Individual
AGE GROUP: Adolescent

REFERENCES

Ren Kneisl, C., and Trigoboff, E. (2009), p. 394.
Stuart, G. W., and Laraia, M. T. (2005), p. 408.

146. CORRECT ANSWER: 2

1. Transferring the client will be disruptive and is not a practical solution.

■ **2. This will draw the nurse's attention to the fact that the two clients have the same last name.**

3. This is not an option and it may not prevent errors.

4. This will not help the nurse distinguish between the two clients with the same last name.

CLASSIFICATION

COMPETENCY CATEGORY: Professional Practice
TAXONOMIC LEVEL: Application
CLIENT TYPE: Group, Population, Community
AGE GROUP: Not applicable

REFERENCES

Potter, P. A., Griffin Perry, A., Ross-Kerr, J. C., and Wood, M. J. (2006), pp. 845, 855.
Potter, P. A., and Griffin Perry, A. (2007), p. 355.

147. CORRECT ANSWER: 4

1. This does not allow for the student to feel valued as part of the team and to ask questions.

2. This does not encourage the student to ask questions and learn from the experienced nurses. It does not foster an exchange of information.

3. This does not encourage the student nurse to ask questions or feel part of the team.

■ **4. This encourages the student to ask questions and allows the nurse to complete her tasks.**

CLASSIFICATION

COMPETENCY CATEGORY: Nurse-Client Partnership

TAXONOMIC LEVEL: Application

CLIENT TYPE: Not applicable

AGE GROUP: Not applicable

REFERENCES

Potter, P. A., and Griffin Perry, A. (2007), p. 637.

Huber, D. (2006), pp. 175, 212.

148. CORRECT ANSWER: 4

1. When working with drug orders, the route has to be considered because the prescriber can make a mistake (e.g., the client is unable to take orally or the drug is not available orally).

2. Never use trailing zeros (1.0 mg), but always use leading zeros (0.25 mg) to prevent unintentional overdose or underdose.

3. The nurse should always contact the person who prescribed the drug for clarification.

■ **4. When working with medication orders, the nurse must take into account any client allergies.**

CLASSIFICATION

COMPETENCY CATEGORY: Changes in Health

TAXONOMIC LEVEL: Application

CLIENT TYPE: Individual

AGE GROUP: Not applicable

REFERENCES

Lilley, L. L., Harrington, S., Snyder, J. S., and Swart, B. (2007), pp. 62-63.

Potter, P. A., Griffin Perry, A., Ross-Kerr, J. C., and Wood, M. J. (2006), pp. 854-857.

149. CORRECT ANSWER: 3

1. Knowing the effect of age on medications allows one to determine a reasonable and predictable pattern in the response of older adults to medications.

2. Tolerance does not contribute to polypharmacy.

■ **3. Studies show that many specialists are prescribing medications that are filled at different pharmacies, so there are few checks on medications that interact with each other.**

4. Although this may be done, it is not the reason for polypharmacy.

CLASSIFICATION

COMPETENCY CATEGORY: Health and Wellness

TAXONOMIC LEVEL: Knowledge/Comprehension

CLIENT TYPE: Group, Population, Community

AGE GROUP: Older Adult

REFERENCES

Ebersole, P., Hess, P., Touhy, T., Jett, K., and Luggen, A. (2008), p. 295.

Lilley, L. L., Harrington, S., Snyder, J. S., and Swart, B. (2007), pp. 41-45.

150. CORRECT ANSWER: 3

1. Hyperkalemia occurs in renal failure.

2. Bedrest is recommended to reduce the metabolic rate.

■ **3. Glomerular filtration rate (GFR) is reduced, leading to fluid retention and overload; therefore, the nurse needs to ascultate for breath sounds.**

4. Fluid overload occurs as a result of decreased GFR.

CLASSIFICATION

COMPETENCY CATEGORY: Changes in Health

TAXONOMIC LEVEL: Application

CLIENT TYPE: Individual

AGE GROUP: Older Adult

REFERENCES

Day, R. A., Paul, P., Williams, B., Smeltzer, S. C., and Bare, B. (2007), pp. 1330-1331.

Mantik Lewis, S., McLean Heitkemper, M., Ruff Dirksen, S., Goldsworthy, S., and Barry, M. A. (2006), pp. 1222-1223.

151. CORRECT ANSWER: 4

1. This response negates the client's belief in alternative therapies and implies that her labour experience will be more painful than she may anticipate.

2. This response encourages the client to remain open-minded about pain relief but may create anxiety about labour.

3. This response supports the client's belief in alternative therapies; however, it implies that she will need medication as well.

■ **4. This response supports the client's belief in alternative therapies, while promoting awareness of safety concerns.**

CLASSIFICATION

COMPETENCY CATEGORY: Nurse-Client Partnership

TAXONOMIC LEVEL: Critical Thinking

CLIENT TYPE: Group, Population, Community

AGE GROUP: Young Adult

REFERENCES

Canadian Nurses Association. (2008), p. 18.

Lium Edelman, C., and Mandle, C. L. (2006), pp. 321-322.

152. CORRECT ANSWER: 3

1. Documentation goes into the medication record.

2. This does not address the issue that a medication error was made, and it is not in the nurse's scope of practice to withhold medication.

■ **3. This acknowledges that an error was made and correctly reported.**

4. The physician should be notified, not the pharmacist.

CLASSIFICATION

COMPETENCY CATEGORY: Professional Practice

TAXONOMIC LEVEL: Application

CLIENT TYPE: Individual

AGE GROUP: Not applicable

REFERENCES

Taylor, C., Lillis, C., and LeMone, P. (2005), p. 132.

Lilley, L. L., Harrington, S., Snyder, J. S., and Swart, B. (2007), p. 64.

153. CORRECT ANSWER: **2**

1. This indicates that Fred does not know his client assignment, which he should have known.

■ **2. This clarifies to the client what Fred's role is and his scope of practice and avoids role confusion.**

3. This does not answer the client's confusion about the roles of the nurses or their scope of practice.

4. This does not indicate or clarify what Fred's role is.

CLASSIFICATION

COMPETENCY CATEGORY: Professional Practice

TAXONOMIC LEVEL: Application

CLIENT TYPE: Individual

AGE GROUP: Not applicable

REFERENCES

Potter, P. A., Griffin Perry, A., Ross-Kerr, J. C., and Wood, M. J. (2006), pp. 1661-1663.

Huber, D. (2006), pp. 61-62.

154. CORRECT ANSWER: **2**

1. This belittles Mrs. Jones' feelings and does not acknowledge her concerns.

■ **2. Emotional support and the nurse's presence can reduce anxiety and lessen dyspnea.**

3. The nurse has shifted focus and is not able to provide adequate emotional support.

4. This may heighten Mrs. Jones' anxiety.

CLASSIFICATION

COMPETENCY CATEGORY: Changes in Health

TAXONOMIC LEVEL: Critical Thinking

CLIENT TYPE: Individual

AGE GROUP: Middle Adult

REFERENCES

Carpenito-Moyet, L. J. (2008), p. 126.

Mantik Lewis, S., McLean Heitkemper, M. M., Ruff Dirksen, S., Goldsworthy, S., and Barry, M. A. (2006), p. 948.

155. CORRECT ANSWER: **2**

1. Morphine sulfate is for pain; Mrs. Ross' pain level is fine.

■ **2. Mrs. Ross is nauseated so she would require dimenhydrinate (Gravol).**

3. Naloxone (Narcan) is used with respiratory depression.

4. Lorazepam (Ativan) is an anti-anxiety agent.

CLASSIFICATION

COMPETENCY CATEGORY: Changes in Health

TAXONOMIC LEVEL: Critical Thinking

CLIENT TYPE: Individual

AGE GROUP: Young Adult

REFERENCES

Hopper Deglin, J., and Hazard Vallerand, A. (2006), p. 312.

Timby, B. K., and Smith, N. E. (2007), p. 823.

156. CORRECT ANSWER: **1**

■ 1. **This is an appropriate nursing action because the nurse has used research to initiate a change in nursing practice.**

2. A questionnaire is not the most effective method to collect information (e.g., poor response rate, literacy level, poor eyesight) and does not initiate a change in practice.

3. This action would increase the health-care team's awareness of the problem but would not create a change in practice.

4. This action would increase the nursing educator's awareness of the problem but would not create a change in practice.

CLASSIFICATION

COMPETENCY CATEGORY: Health and Wellness

TAXONOMIC LEVEL: Application

CLIENT TYPE: Group, Population, Community

AGE GROUP: Adult of Advanced Age

REFERENCES

Black, J. M., and Hokanson Hawks, J. (2009), p. 266.

Meiner, S. E., and Lueckenotte, A. G. (2006), p. 388.

157. CORRECT ANSWER: **3**

1. This may assist with keeping the air clean of impurities but clean air has not been shown to prevent sudden infant death syndrome (SIDS).

2. Reduced body temperature has not been shown to potentiate SIDS. Overheating has been associated with SIDS.

■ 3. **Recent studies have shown an increased incidence of SIDS in infants who sleep on their stomachs. There is no evidence that sleeping on the back is harmful to healthy infants.**

4. Use of an infant monitor will not prevent SIDS.

CLASSIFICATION

COMPETENCY CATEGORY: Health and Wellness

TAXONOMIC LEVEL: Knowledge/Comprehension

CLIENT TYPE: Group, Population, Community

AGE GROUP: Newborn and Infants

REFERENCES

Leonard Lowdermilk, D., and Perry, E. S. (2006), p. 606.

Hockenberry, M. J., and Wilson, D. (2009), p. 400.

158. CORRECT ANSWER: **4**

1. Calling the client's family would compromise confidentiality if the nurse's suspicions are unfounded.

2. Filing a report with the security department does not share the information with the health-care team.

3. The nurse could report the incident to the physician at a later time, not immediately.

■ 4. **Written documentation is the best way to observe the client consistently for further behaviours and to communicate with the rest of the team.**

CLASSIFICATION

COMPETENCY CATEGORY: Professional Practice

TAXONOMIC LEVEL: Application

CLIENT TYPE: Individual

AGE GROUP: Not applicable

REFERENCES

Potter, P. A., Griffin Perry, A., Ross-Kerr, J. C., and Wood, M. J. (2006), pp. 97, 116.

Elkin, M. K., Griffin Perry, A., and Potter, P. A. (2007), p. 11.

159. CORRECT ANSWER: 4

1. The physician's behaviour is unprofessional and unacceptable.

2. This action indicates that the nurse was in error and reinforces the behaviour.

3. This would not be appropriate at this time because it does not deal with the immediacy of the problem.

■ **4. This is a form of harassment and the nurse needs to report the action to the nurse-in-charge.**

CLASSIFICATION

COMPETENCY CATEGORY: Professional Practice

TAXONOMIC LEVEL: Application

CLIENT TYPE: Individual

AGE GROUP: Not applicable

REFERENCES

Marriner-Tomey, A. (2008), pp. 112-113.

Huber, D. (2006), pp. 681, 689.

160. CORRECT ANSWER: 4

1. This overlooks the fact that Mr. Davies may be having a blood transfusion reaction.

2. This overlooks the fact that Mr. Davies may be having a blood transfusion reaction.

3. Documentation is not a priority action. This overlooks the fact that Mr. Davies may be having a blood transfusion reaction.

■ **4. Anxiety, tachycardia, shortness of breath and a red face may be signs and symptoms of a major blood transfusion reaction.**

CLASSIFICATION

COMPETENCY CATEGORY: Changes in Health

TAXONOMIC LEVEL: Critical Thinking

CLIENT TYPE: Individual

AGE GROUP: Middle Adult

REFERENCES

Mantik Lewis, S., McLean Heitkemper, M., Ruff Dirksen, S., Goldsworthy, S., and Barry, M. A. (2006), p. 756.

Potter, P. A., Griffin Perry, A., Ross-Kerr, J. C., and Wood, M. J. (2006), p. 1203.

161. CORRECT ANSWER: 2

1. The nurse should always explain the procedure to the client first.

■ **2. The nurse should always explain the procedure to the client first.**

3. This is not the priority action because consent has not been obtained.

4. The procedure must always be explained to the client first.

CLASSIFICATION

COMPETENCY CATEGORY: Changes in Health

TAXONOMIC LEVEL: Critical Thinking

CLIENT TYPE: Individual

AGE GROUP: Adult of Advanced Age

REFERENCES

Potter, P. A., Griffin Perry, A., Ross-Kerr, J. C., and Wood, M. J. (2006), p. 906.

Elkin, M. K., Perry, A. G., and Potter, P. A. (2007), p. 596.

162. CORRECT ANSWER: 1

■ 1. **Warm-up exercises increase cardiovascular efficiency, reduce fatigue and increase mental alertness. This is important at the beginning of a teaching session.**

2. Although increased socialization is an important benefit of exercise, the nurse's primary rationale is to increase mental alertness.

3. Although decreasing immobility is an important benefit of exercise, the nurse's primary rationale is to increase mental alertness.

4. Although promoting good sleep habits is an important benefit of exercise, the nurse's primary rationale is to increase mental alertness.

CLASSIFICATION

COMPETENCY CATEGORY: Health and Wellness
TAXONOMIC LEVEL: Knowledge/Comprehension
CLIENT TYPE: Group, Population, Community
AGE GROUP: Older Adult

REFERENCES

Ebersole, P., Hess, P., Touhy, T., Jett, K., and Luggen, A. (2008), p. 143.
Hoffman Wold, G. (2008), pp. 310-311.

163. CORRECT ANSWER: 1

■ 1. **Studies have shown that home care is more cost effective and health effective.**

2. Interprofessional care is possible within the home environment.

3. There is no vaccine for methicillin-resistant *Staphylococcus aureus* (MRSA); precautions should be taken to prevent the spread of the microorganism.

4. Consistency in caregivers and the environment can lessen the spread of microorganisms.

CLASSIFICATION

COMPETENCY CATEGORY: Health and Wellness
TAXONOMIC LEVEL: Critical Thinking
CLIENT TYPE: Family
AGE GROUP: Adult of Advanced Age

REFERENCES

Mantik Lewis, S., McLean Heitkemper, M., Ruff Dirksen, S., Goldsworthy, S., and Barry, M. A. (2006), p. 84.
Stanhope, M., and Lancaster, J. (2008), pp. 863-887.

164. CORRECT ANSWER: 2

1. This is not in the client's best interest and ignores best practice.

■ 2. **An order for best practice dressing change needs to be obtained first. This ensures that the client's needs are being met with the best practice method.**

3. An order change should be obtained prior to changing practice.

4. This does not deal with the immediacy of the issue and does not ensure that the client is getting the best quality of care.

CLASSIFICATION

COMPETENCY CATEGORY: Professional Practice
TAXONOMIC LEVEL: Critical Thinking
CLIENT TYPE: Individual
AGE GROUP: Not applicable

REFERENCES

Potter, P. A., Griffin Perry, A., Ross-Kerr, J. C., and Wood, M. J. (2006), p. 1539.
Elkin, M. K., Griffin Perry, A., and Potter, P. A. (2007), p. 518.

165. CORRECT ANSWER: 4

1. Although weight loss will treat sleep apnea, and clients may not have to use the therapy, there is no cure.

2. Sleep apnea is associated with age; however, it does not worsen with age.

3. Dedicated use allows the client to feel more rested and less fatigued. Regular use will not decrease the need for therapy. When clients do not use the therapy, they become fatigued.

■ **4. With sleep apnea the throat muscles relax, shutting the airway and causing apneic periods.**

CLASSIFICATION

COMPETENCY CATEGORY: Professional Practice

TAXONOMIC LEVEL: Critical Thinking

CLIENT TYPE: Individual

AGE GROUP: Older Adult

REFERENCES

Miller, C. A. (2009), pp. 510-523.

Potter, P. A., Griffin Perry, A., Ross-Kerr, J. C., and Wood, M. J. (2006), p. 1215.

166. CORRECT ANSWER: 3

1. It is unlikely that the annual flu vaccine will be specific to the strain of virus causing the flu.

2. It is unlikely that there will be sufficient antiviral medication for everyone. Also it may take four to six months to produce an antiviral medication that will be specific to the virus causing the outbreak.

■ **3. Public gatherings will be suspended or limited. Schools will be closed to prevent the spread of the flu.**

4. The pandemic is likely to hit many communities at the same time, and additional medical staff may not be available. Travel of people from one area to another will aid in spreading the pandemic.

CLASSIFICATION

COMPETENCY CATEGORY: Health and Wellness

TAXONOMIC LEVEL: Knowledge/Comprehension

CLIENT TYPE: Group, Population, Community

AGE GROUP: Not applicable

REFERENCES

Cherry, B., and Jacob, S. R. (2008), pp. 324-325

Stanhope, M., and Lancaster, J. (2006), pp. 522-523.

167. CORRECT ANSWER: 2

1. Bumping into furniture is an immediate safety issue and needs to be addressed. This action would take time.

■ **2. This situation is a safety issue for older adults, and it should be addressed immediately at the administrative level to decrease the risk for older adults until a more detailed assessment can take place.**

3. The chairs are placed for the convenience of the older adults waiting for others. The placement of the chairs may not be the issue, but rather the type of chair or chair leg may be the safety issue for older adults with declining vision.

4. Discussion and administration is the first step toward assessment, which is necessary to allow for individual differences in normal physical changes with aging.

CLASSIFICATION

COMPETENCY CATEGORY: Professional Practice

TAXONOMIC LEVEL: Critical Thinking

CLIENT TYPE: Group, Population, Community

AGE GROUP: Adult of Advanced Age

REFERENCES

Ebersole, P., Hess, P., Touhy, T., Jett, K., and Luggen, A. (2008), pp. 348-350.

Meiner, S. E., and Lueckenotte, A. G. (2006), pp. 257-258.

168. CORRECT ANSWER: 4

1. Although pairing is a good method to foster exchange of information, it is not always effective as it does not match the strengths and weaknesses of the participants.

2. This would only facilitate information between the nurse educator and new staff members. Also, the nurse educator cannot mentor the whole group.

3. Although it would be beneficial to determine the needs of the group, this does not foster collaboration, interaction or exchange of information with the unit staff.

■ **4. This would allow both groups to interact and encourage questioning and an exchange of information between both groups.**

CLASSIFICATION

COMPETENCY CATEGORY: Nurse-Client Partnership
TAXONOMIC LEVEL: Application
CLIENT TYPE: Group, Population, Community
AGE GROUP: Not applicable

REFERENCES

Canadian Nurses Association. (2008), 41-42.
Hibberd, J. M., and Smith, D. L. (2006), p. 129.

169. CORRECT ANSWER: 3

1. The author, title and qualifications should be indicated on the site.

2. A site sponsored by a company may promote the company's product. The information may also be biased.

■ **3. Information is changing frequently and should be updated on the Internet site. This will ensure that the information is current.**

4. Testimonials may be biased and contain misinformation.

CLASSIFICATION

COMPETENCY CATEGORY: Professional Practice
TAXONOMIC LEVEL: Knowledge/Comprehension
CLIENT TYPE: Not applicable
AGE GROUP: Not applicable

REFERENCES

Stanhope, M., and Lancaster, J. (2006), p. 206.
Kittrell Chitty, K., and Perry Black, B. (2007), pp. 309-310.

170. CORRECT ANSWER: 1

■ **1. Cystitis is a lower urinary tract infection. These are some of the most common ways that bacteria are able to enter the bladder.**

2. These are not commonly associated with bacterial infection of the bladder.

3. These are types of urinary incontinence that could cause cystitis but are not the most common causes.

4. These are risk factors for urinary tract infections but not the most common for cystitis.

CLASSIFICATION

COMPETENCY CATEGORY: Changes in Health
TAXONOMIC LEVEL: Knowledge/Comprehension
CLIENT TYPE: Not applicable
AGE GROUP: Not applicable

REFERENCES

Timby, B. K., and Smith, N. E. (2007), pp. 1153-1161.
Day, R. A., Paul, P., Williams, B., Smeltzer, S. C., and Bare, B. (2007), pp. 1315-1316.

171. CORRECT ANSWER: 3

1. The interaction needs to be reported.

2. Treating side effects will not address the underlying problem.

■ 3. **This is a professional and legal obligation of the nurse to prevent future injury to the client.**

4. Providing oxygen will not resolve the underlying problem. This needs to be reported and documented first.

CLASSIFICATION

COMPETENCY CATEGORY: Changes in Health

TAXONOMIC LEVEL: Critical Thinking

CLIENT TYPE: Individual

AGE GROUP: Middle Adult

REFERENCES

Quinn Youngkin, E., Sawin, K. J., Kissinger, J. F., and Israel, D. S. (2005), pp. 89-91.

Brophy, K. M., Scarlett-Ferguson, H., and Webber, K. S. (2008), pp. 25-26.

172. CORRECT ANSWER: 4

1. This may alleviate pain in the short term but will not eliminate it.

2. Placebos will not bind to opioid receptors and thus will not reduce pain in this manner.

3. Giving a placebo is unethical and can destroy the trust the client has in the health-care providers.

■ 4. **The use of a placebo will destroy the trust that the client has in the health-care system. This is an unethical practice.**

CLASSIFICATION

COMPETENCY CATEGORY: Professional Practice

TAXONOMIC LEVEL: Critical Thinking

CLIENT TYPE: Individual

AGE GROUP: Young Adult

REFERENCES

Black, J. M., and Hokanson Hawks, J. (2009), pp. 357-358.

Mantik Lewis, S., McLean Heitkemper, M., Ruff Dirksen, S., Goldsworthy, S., and Barry, M. A. (2006), p. 157.

173. CORRECT ANSWER: 1

■ 1. **The variety of life experiences and symptoms associated with physical changes of aging make it difficult to determine the emotional health status of older adults.**

2. Older adults are not well served in the current mental health system.

3. Anxiety disorders are very common in older adults.

4. Suicide is a significant problem among older white men whenever they confront a trauma or catastrophe.

CLASSIFICATION

COMPETENCY CATEGORY: Health and Wellness

TAXONOMIC LEVEL: Knowledge/Comprehension

CLIENT TYPE: Group, Population, Community

AGE GROUP: Older Adult

REFERENCES

Ebersole, P., Hess, P., Touhy, T., Jett, K., and Luggen, A. (2008), pp. 598-600.

Meiner, S. E., and Lueckenotte, A. G. (2006), pp. 281-285.

174. CORRECT ANSWER: 2

1. This is premature and is taking the apparent improvement at face value.

■ **2. A sudden improvement in mood in a deeply depressed person should alert the nurse to conduct an assessment because it can mean that the person has made a decision and now has the energy to take his or her own life. Moreover, the second or third week of antidepressant therapy is a time of increased risk for suicide because clients have increased energy but their depression is not resolved.**

3. Antidepressant medications can take up to four weeks to take effect. The first changes usually seen relate to motor behaviour, not to mood. Often the first effects of the antidepressant give the client enough energy to consider suicide.

4. The nurse must act immediately to assess the potential for suicide.

CLASSIFICATION

COMPETENCY CATEGORY: Changes in Health
TAXONOMIC LEVEL: Critical Thinking
CLIENT TYPE: Individual
AGE GROUP: Middle Adult

REFERENCES

Ren Kneisl, C., and Trigoboff, E. (2009), p. 630.
Rebraca Shives, L. (2005), p. 494.

175. CORRECT ANSWER: 1

■ **1. Nausea and abdominal distension are signs that the nasogastric (NG) tube is not maintaining gastrointestinal decompression.**

2. This does not mean that the NG tube is not functioning effectively.

3. This does not indicate that the NG tube is not functioning effectively.

4. This is a normal finding.

CLASSIFICATION

COMPETENCY CATEGORY: Changes in Health
TAXONOMIC LEVEL: Knowledge/Comprehension
CLIENT TYPE: Individual
AGE GROUP: Not applicable

REFERENCES

Potter, P. A., Griffin Perry, A., Ross-Kerr, J. C., and Wood, M. J. (2006), p. 1421.
Griffin Perry, A., and Potter, P. A. (2006), pp. 1142-1143.

176. CORRECT ANSWER: 4

1. Although this could be a sign of hemorrhage, it is not the earliest sign. Vital signs are the most crucial to assess.

2. This is a normal finding of a cesarian section (i.e., the entire placenta has been delivered).

3. Hematuria is not uncommon, especially if cesarian follows a failed forceps or long labour; decrease in BP less than 80 mmHg is significant.

■ **4. This is indicative of possible hemorrhage. Fundus should contract after delivery to prevent hemorrhage.**

CLASSIFICATION

COMPETENCY CATEGORY: Changes in Health
TAXONOMIC LEVEL: Critical Thinking
CLIENT TYPE: Individual
AGE GROUP: Young Adult

REFERENCES

Pillitteri, A. (2007), p. 579.
Evans, R. J., Evans, M. K., Brown, Y. M. R., and Orshan S. A. (2009), pp. 740-741, 707.

177. CORRECT ANSWER: 2

1. The drug therapy will continue until Mrs. Osbourne's sputum is negative for bacilli.

■ **2. The daughter is on vacation and may be contagious.**

3. Anyone who has had contact with Mrs. Osbourne or her family in the past 3 months has to be notified and tested.

4. Staff members have to be tested, but the skin test may not be the test of choice.

CLASSIFICATION

COMPETENCY CATEGORY: Health and Wellness

TAXONOMIC LEVEL: Critical Thinking

CLIENT TYPE: Family

AGE GROUP: Adult of Advanced Age

REFERENCES

Nies, M. A., and McEwen, M. (2007), pp. 524-525.

Stanhope, M., and Lancaster, J. (2006), p. 536

178. CORRECT ANSWER: 3

1. This intervention is important to determine the degree of injury to the extremity. The client should have an evaluation of neurological or abdominal injuries before the extremity is treated.

2. Vital signs are very important in determining injury because the client is pale and anxious, but this is not the most critical potential complication.

■ **3. Any client involved in a motor vehicle collision with direct trauma to the head or the neck must be considered to have a spinal cord injury. Initial action should be a rapid assessment of the neck and immobilization.**

4. This intervention promotes circulation and helps to prevent further injury, but it is not the initial action.

CLASSIFICATION

COMPETENCY CATEGORY: Changes in Health

TAXONOMIC LEVEL: Critical Thinking

CLIENT TYPE: Individual

AGE GROUP: Older Adult

REFERENCES

Smeltzer, S. C., and Bare, B. G. (2007), p. 1938

Timby, B. K., and Smith, N. E. (2007), p. 733.

179. CORRECT ANSWER: 3

1. This is true, but it also presents a condescending attitude to Ms. Jones. It does not answer her question.

2. It may be true that it is a hospital policy; however, this answer may not satisfy Ms. Jones.

■ **3. This is one of the major reasons for electronic fetal monitoring during induction.**

4. This response may give Ms. Jones undue cause for alarm. Despite all its capabilities, the electronic fetal monitor does not give the staff plenty of time to deliver the baby.

CLASSIFICATION

COMPETENCY CATEGORY: Changes in Health

TAXONOMIC LEVEL: Knowledge/Comprehension

CLIENT TYPE: Family

AGE GROUP: The Period Between Preconception and Birth

REFERENCES

Leifer, G. (2007), p. 288.

Pillitteri, A. (2007), p. 520.

180. CORRECT ANSWER: 2

1. Although this is urgent, dehiscence does not routinely require surgery.

■ **2. Cleansing, packing and/or redressing the wound is all that is required because this client is in the proliferative phase of wound healing, occurring at 5 to 21 days.**

3. Although splinting may help prevent dehiscence, this does not address what to do after dehiscence has occurred.

4. This is the emergency action for wound evisceration, not dehiscence.

CLASSIFICATION

COMPETENCY CATEGORY: Changes in Health

TAXONOMIC LEVEL: Critical Thinking

CLIENT TYPE: Individual

AGE GROUP: Middle Adult

REFERENCES

Black, J. M., and Hokanson Hawks, J. (2009), p. 321.

Potter, P. A., Griffin Perry, A., Ross-Kerr, J. C., and Wood, M. J. (2006), p. 1508.

---

181. CORRECT ANSWER: 4

1. It measures gross body movements of the fetus.

2. Colour is not determined, but the size of the pocket of amniotic fluid volume is measured.

3. This is not part of biophysical profile (BPP).

■ **4. The non-stress test is part of the BPP.**

CLASSIFICATION

COMPETENCY CATEGORY: Changes in Health

TAXONOMIC LEVEL: Knowledge/Comprehension

CLIENT TYPE: Individual

AGE GROUP: The Period Between Preconception and Birth

REFERENCES

Wong, D. L., Perry, S. E., Hockenberry, M. J., Lowdermilk, D. L., and Wilson, D. (2006), p. 223.

Leonard Lowdermilk, D., and Perry, E. S. (2006), p. 648.

---

182. CORRECT ANSWER: 1

■ **1. A nurse-client relationship cannot cross the therapeutic boundaries.**

2. The alternative of meeting in a public place does not negate the fact that the relationship has crossed therapeutic boundaries.

3. The nurse does not need to check with the supervisor to know that therapeutic boundaries would be crossed.

4. Accepting a personal invitation from a client's family crosses the therapeutic relationship boundaries.

CLASSIFICATION

COMPETENCY CATEGORY: Nurse-Client Partnership

TAXONOMIC LEVEL: Application

CLIENT TYPE: Family

AGE GROUP: Adult of Advanced Age

REFERENCES

Arnold, E. C., and Underman Boggs, K. (2007), pp. 95-97.

Stuart, G. W., and Laraia, M. T. (2009), pp. 41-42.

183. CORRECT ANSWER: 1

■ 1. These are all signs of sepsis in the newborn. Temperature is unstable and can be low or high; bradycardia is common. Presence of petechiae may be evidence of hemorrhage seen in advanced infection. Poor feeding is common as are respiratory problems. Prolonged labour is also a risk factor for neonatal sepsis.

2. Petechiae is not a sign of cold stress, and Brooke's temperature has risen above 36 ºC.

3. Petechiae, jitteriness and increased RR are not signs of ineffective breastfeeding or hyperbilirubinemia.

4. These are not all signs of hypoglycemia.

CLASSIFICATION

COMPETENCY CATEGORY: Changes in Health

TAXONOMIC LEVEL: Critical Thinking

CLIENT TYPE: Individual

AGE GROUP: Newborn and Infants

REFERENCES

Leonard Lowdermilk, D., and Perry, E. S. (2006), p. 892.

Wong, D. L., Perry, S. E., Hockenberry, M. J., Lowdermilk, D. L., and Wilson, D. (2006), pp. 832-834.

184. CORRECT ANSWER: 2

1. Access to health care is important for all Canadians in the prevention of illness; it is not the most effective means of promoting health.

■ 2. Research has shown that nursing interventions in health promotion programs are more effective if they relate to the individual's personal definition of health. Focus groups are effective in providing an accurate picture of community perspectives.

3. Primary prevention strategies focus on risk factors and are not necessary for success in this health promotion program.

4. Changes associated with aging (e.g., changes in visual acuity) may prevent some older adults from providing written input into the program.

CLASSIFICATION

COMPETENCY CATEGORY: Health and Wellness

TAXONOMIC LEVEL: Application

CLIENT TYPE: Group, Population, Community

AGE GROUP: Older Adult

REFERENCES

Stanhope, M., and Lancaster, J. (2008). (1st Canadian ed.), pp. 73, 273-274.

Nies, M. A., and McEwen, M. (2007), pp. 108-111.

185. CORRECT ANSWER: 1

■ 1. This indicates the mother's interest in learning.

2. A support group does not provide the clinical information needed.

3. This does not indicate the mother's readiness to learn and does not indicate her involvement or ownership of the experience.

4. This minimizes the potential complications of the son's condition.

CLASSIFICATION

COMPETENCY CATEGORY: Nurse-Client Partnership

TAXONOMIC LEVEL: Application

CLIENT TYPE: Family

AGE GROUP: Newborn and Infants

REFERENCES

Potter, P. A., Griffin Perry, A., Ross-Kerr, J. C., and Wood, M. J. (2006), p. 324.

Maurer, F. A., and Smith, C. (2005), pp. 456-458.

186. CORRECT ANSWER: 1

■ 1. **The symptoms of schizophrenia are described as positive (excesses, such as hallucinations and delusions) and negative (deficits or loss of normal functioning). The negative symptoms present as avolition, affective flattening, anhedonia and alogia.**

2. This answer is judgmental and shows failure to apply knowledge of the illness. This is conjecture and labelling, and the nurse should never engage in either one.

3. Antipsychotic medication can have sedating effects, but there is nothing in the question to suggest a change in medication. Mr. Godfrey has been treated for some time and it is likely that the dose would have been adjusted if he had experienced this side effect.

4. The symptoms described are typical of the negative symptoms of schizophrenia and, while similar to those of depression, they are different. People with schizophrenia can have a second diagnosis, but there is no indication of this in the question.

CLASSIFICATION

COMPETENCY CATEGORY: Changes in Health

TAXONOMIC LEVEL: Application

CLIENT TYPE: Family

AGE GROUP: Young Adult

REFERENCES

Ren Kneisl, C., and Trigoboff, E. (2009), p. 374.

Austin, W., and Boyd, M. A. (2008), p. 291.

187. CORRECT ANSWER: 4

1. A health framework focusing on health promotion and prevention is the focus of primary health care (PHC) and not simply a disease-oriented approach.

2. PHC extends beyond the health system to other societal systems (e.g., political systems) that create conditions in which health can flourish.

3. PHC shifts the emphasis of health care to the people themselves, within the community, empowering them to shape their own lives.

■ 4. **Homeless people hesitate to use medical services; therefore, community groups (e.g., soup kitchens) may help the health-care team gain access to this population. Appropriate use of services is a principle of PHC.**

CLASSIFICATION

COMPETENCY CATEGORY: Health and Wellness

TAXONOMIC LEVEL: Application

CLIENT TYPE: Group, Population, Community

AGE GROUP: Not applicable

REFERENCES

Stanhope, M., and Lancaster, J. (2008), pp. 2-6.

Potter, P. A., Griffin Perry, A., Ross-Kerr, J. C., and Wood, M. J. (2006), p. 30.

188. CORRECT ANSWER: 2

1. Although this is a useful strategy, there is no collaboration and no assurance that it will be implemented.

■ **2. Involving the parents, teachers and children will ensure community ownership and is likely to increase participation.**

3. What is in the vending machines is more important than the machines themselves.

4. This does not ensure all children benefit from health teaching. Moreover, it is derogatory and does not involve all stakeholders.

CLASSIFICATION

COMPETENCY CATEGORY: Health and Wellness

TAXONOMIC LEVEL: Application

CLIENT TYPE: Group, Population, Community

AGE GROUP: Older Child

REFERENCES

Nies, M. A., and McEwen, M. (2007), pp. 254-257.

Maurer, F. A., and Smith, C. (2009), pp. 480-481.

189. CORRECT ANSWER: 4

1. Distraction is useful with less severe pain levels; however, analgesia is required after surgery.

2. Bonding cannot occur if the mother is distracted by pain. It is important to treat the pain first in an effort to promote bonding.

3. A warm blanket may be comforting with less severe pain levels; however, analgesia is required after surgery.

■ **4. This intervention assists in pain management and may promote mother-infant bonding.**

CLASSIFICATION

COMPETENCY CATEGORY: Changes in Health

TAXONOMIC LEVEL: Critical Thinking

CLIENT TYPE: Family

AGE GROUP: Young Adult

REFERENCES

Pillitteri, A. (2007), p. 577.

Leonard Lowdermilk, D., and Perry, E. S. (2007), p. 961.

190. CORRECT ANSWER: 2

1. This does not follow the proper line of authority. The nurse's immediate supervisor should be told first.

■ **2. Because the colleague has already been reprimanded by the nurse-in-charge, it is important that this authority be made aware of the continuing problems in this area.**

3. The nurse has already been reprimanded. Therefore, the next level of authority has to be involved.

4. This action is appropriate for short-term client safety but the incident must be reported to ensure long-term client safety.

CLASSIFICATION

COMPETENCY CATEGORY: Professional Practice

TAXONOMIC LEVEL: Critical Thinking

CLIENT TYPE: Individual

AGE GROUP: Newborn and Infants

REFERENCES

Potter, P. A., Griffin Perry, A., Ross-Kerr, J. C., and Wood, M. J. (2006), pp. 150-151.

Huber, D. (2006), p. 516.

191. CORRECT ANSWER: 1

■ 1. **Nitroglycerin is the treatment for angina attacks if the systolic blood pressure is not lower or equal to 90 mmHg.**

2. Assessing the client's level of pain is very important but acetaminophen (Tylenol) is not the drug of choice for a client with a known history of cardiac disease.

3. Pain is not common following a myocardial infarction and sometimes is an indicator of complications.

4. These are appropriate interventions but treating Mr. Stone's angina right away is important.

CLASSIFICATION

COMPETENCY CATEGORY: Changes in Health
TAXONOMIC LEVEL: Application
CLIENT TYPE: Individual
AGE GROUP: Middle Adult

REFERENCES

Smeltzer, S. C., Bare, B., Hinkle, J. L., and Cheever, K. H. (2007), pp. 724-725.

Black, J. M., and Hokanson Hawks, J. (2009), p. 1487.

192. CORRECT ANSWER: 4

1. Mcpcridine (Demerol) is not recommended for older adults because of accumulation of toxic metabolites.

2. Nalaxone is given when respiratory depression occurs, not agitation.

3. This is not the most likely cause of Mrs. Singh's agitation.

■ 4. **Meperidine (Demerol) is not recommended for use in older adults because of accumulation of toxic metabolites. Symptoms of toxicity include agitation and tremulousness.**

CLASSIFICATION

COMPETENCY CATEGORY: Changes in Health
TAXONOMIC LEVEL: Critical Thinking
CLIENT TYPE: Individual
AGE GROUP: Older Adult

REFERENCES

Brophy, K. M., Scarlett-Ferguson, H., and Webber, K. S. (2008), p. 90.

Abrams, A. C., Pennington, S. S., and Lammon, B. (2007), p. 88.

193. CORRECT ANSWER: 1

■ 1. **Severe respiratory failure leads to hypoxia. Hypoxia causes bradycardia, which is a late sign in children.**

2. Although a cardinal sign of respiratory failure, tachycardia is considered an early sign in children.

3. Although a cardinal sign of respiratory failure, restlessness is considered an early sign in children.

4. Although a sign of respiratory failure, nasal flaring is considered an early sign in children.

CLASSIFICATION

COMPETENCY CATEGORY: Changes in Health
TAXONOMIC LEVEL: Knowledge/Comprehension
CLIENT TYPE: Individual
AGE GROUP: Young Child

REFERENCES

Hockenberry, M. J., and Wilson, D. (2007), p. 1302.

Wong, D. L., Perry, S. E., Hockenberry, M. J., Lowdermilk, D. L., and Wilson, D. (2006), p. 1463.

194. CORRECT ANSWER: **4**

1. This is a good stress management technique, but it is less effective without adequate self-awareness.

2. Talking with others may not be effective and it deflects responsibility to take direct action.

3. The client may not recognize that there is a problem.

■ **4. Stress can be best controlled when the client recognizes that it is being experienced.**

CLASSIFICATION

COMPETENCY CATEGORY: Health and Wellness

TAXONOMIC LEVEL: Knowledge/Comprehension

CLIENT TYPE: Group, Population, Community

AGE GROUP: Not applicable

REFERENCES

Potter, P. A., and Griffin Perry, A. (2007), pp. 600-601.

Varcolis, E. M., Carson, V. B., and Shoemaker, N. C. (2006), p. 296.

195. CORRECT ANSWER: **2**

1. This is not recommended. Smoke and toxins released from cigarette smoke are difficult to control.

■ **2. The smoke released from a burning cigarette has more toxins and is more dangerous to health than inhaled smoke.**

3. The smoke and toxins released from cigarettes are difficult to control even in enclosed environments.

4. The smoke and toxins released from cigarettes are difficult to control even in well-ventilated spaces.

CLASSIFICATION

COMPETENCY CATEGORY: Health and Wellness

TAXONOMIC LEVEL: Knowledge/Comprehension

CLIENT TYPE: Family

AGE GROUP: Young Child

REFERENCES

Allender, J. A., and Walton Spradley, B. (2005), p. 602.

Hockenberry, M. J., and Wilson, D. (2007), p. 1352.

196. CORRECT ANSWER: **3**

1. This is correct, but responsiveness must be determined initially.

2. This is correct, but is not the initial action.

■ **3. Determining responsiveness is the initial action.**

4. This manoeuvre is done in a foreign-body airway obstruction.

CLASSIFICATION

COMPETENCY CATEGORY: Changes in Health

TAXONOMIC LEVEL: Application

CLIENT TYPE: Individual

AGE GROUP: Middle Adult

REFERENCES

Mantik Lewis, S., McLean Heitkemper, M., Ruff Dirksen, S., Graber O'Brien, P., and Bucher, L. (2007), p. 1848.

Hopkins, T., and Myers, E. (2008), p. 169.

197. CORRECT ANSWER: 2

1. Kindergarten children like stimulation and learn most effectively when it seems like play. An explanation or demonstration does not engage the children's attention.

■ **2. The most characteristic and pervasive preschool activity is imitative, imaginative and dramatic play. Erikson's developmental task for this period is to gain a sense of initiative or learn how to do things.**

3. Although this might catch their attention, the children may not be able to make the connection between the poster and their handwashing. This strategy would be more effective for an older age group.

4. Although a video can be part of a child's learning, it should be used with parental or teacher supervision and only for short periods of time.

CLASSIFICATION

COMPETENCY CATEGORY: Health and Wellness
TAXONOMIC LEVEL: Application
CLIENT TYPE: Group, Population, Community
AGE GROUP: Young Child

REFERENCES

Hockenberry, M. J., and Wilson, D. (2007), p. 649.
Bastable, S. (2008), p. 162.

198. CORRECT ANSWER: 1

■ **1. Acknowledging the group's feelings demonstrates respect for human dignity and fosters an appropriate learning environment.**

2. This avoids the issue and does not decrease the apprehension.

3. This is a judgmental statement; it avoids the issue and may not be common in all members. It still does not decrease the apprehension.

4. This avoids the issue and fails to address the embarrassment and apprehension.

CLASSIFICATION

COMPETENCY CATEGORY: Nurse-Client Partnership
TAXONOMIC LEVEL: Critical Thinking
CLIENT TYPE: Group, Population, Community
AGE GROUP: Older Adult

REFERENCES

Riley, J. B. (2008), p. 100.
Canadian Nurses Association. (2008), p. 13.

199. CORRECT ANSWER: 3

1. This appears judgmental and does not respect Mrs. Lee's desire to try different treatments.

2. This is not a sufficient action given the amount of weight loss.

■ **3. Mrs. Lee has the right to try different treatments but is more likely to take medication if she understands how it works and what the link is between taking medication and the ability to prepare meals.**

4. The nurse is not practising to full scope and is deferring responsibility. The nurse should allow Mrs. Lee to make her own decisions regarding contacting her physician.

CLASSIFICATION

COMPETENCY CATEGORY: Changes in Health

TAXONOMIC LEVEL: Critical Thinking

CLIENT TYPE: Individual

AGE GROUP: Middle Adult

REFERENCES

Brophy, K. M., Scarlett-Ferguson, H., and Webber, K. S. (2008), p. 124.

Potter, P. A., Griffin Perry, A., Ross-Kerr, J. C., and Wood, M. J. (2006), p. 854.

200. CORRECT ANSWER: 4

1. The focus is on prolonging life rather than symptom management.

2. This does not address the husband's concerns.

3. The focus is on prolonging life.

■ **4. At end of life, basal metabolic rate is decreased, but the client does not experience thirst. The supportive measures listed are appropriate.**

CLASSIFICATION

COMPETENCY CATEGORY: Changes in Health

TAXONOMIC LEVEL: Critical Thinking

CLIENT TYPE: Family

AGE GROUP: Older Adult

REFERENCES

Potter, P. A., Griffin Perry, A., Ross-Kerr, J. C., and Wood, M. J. (2006), p. 529.

Day, R. A., Paul, P., Williams, B., Smeltzer, S. C and Bare, B. (2007), p. 392.

END OF INDEPENDENT QUESTIONS RATIONALES

END OF THE BOOK

CHAPTER 8:
CRNE READINESS TEST

■ CRNE READINESS TEST

The CRNE Readiness Test will help you assess your readiness to take the CRNE. Available in either English or French, the readiness test is an online simulated CRNE in a shortened format. The readiness test is composed of 100 multiple-choice questions. The questions on the readiness test are matched with the CRNE in terms of level of difficulty and are presented in the same proportions as the CRNE with respect to the competency categories, levels of cognitive ability and case-based versus independent (stand-alone) questions.

The readiness test provides you with an opportunity to take real exam questions presented in a manner similar to those on the CRNE. Although the actual CRNE is a paper-and-pencil exam, this test is done completely online. Doing the test online allows you to receive an instant overall percentage score and sub-scores by CRNE competency category. You will also be given the range of percentages required to pass the CRNE since June 2000.

The CRNE Readiness Test is available for purchase through the CNA website at http://readiness.cna-aiic.ca/.

■ WHAT SHOULD I EXPECT WHEN TAKING THE CRNE READINESS TEST?

Once you have purchased the test, you will be sent an e-mail with a confirmation of payment, a password and log-in information. After you log in, follow the instructions on the screen to begin the test. When you start the test, you will receive the first of a sequence of 100 multiple-choice questions. Each multiple-choice question has four options to choose from. To make your choice, click the circle beside the option you want to select. The questions appear either as independent (stand-alone) questions or as part of a series of three to five case-based questions. As you complete the questions, you have the ability to flag the questions you want to return to.

The readiness test is most useful when taken under test-like conditions. You should adhere to the time limits and not use any notes or textbooks when taking the test. The test comes equipped with a timer so you can monitor how you are doing in terms of time remaining to complete the test. You will be shown your time at the end of the test. If you have to stop the test before completion, you will be able to return to the test later, provided you have not yet submitted your answers. The timer will start again when you return. Make sure that you do not submit your test until you are ready.

You should take the readiness test by yourself at a time when you do not anticipate interruptions. The prediction of readiness to take the CRNE will be meaningful and useful only if you follow these instructions and complete the readiness test without any assistance.

■ WHAT WILL MY RESULTS LOOK LIKE?

Once you have completed the readiness test and submitted your responses for scoring, you will be shown your profile results. Your results profile will include:

• the overall percentage obtained;

• the percentages needed to pass the CRNE since June 2000;

• the number of questions and percentage of questions answered correctly in each competency category; and

• links to access more information on each competency category.

You can also click "View all multiple-choice questions and answers" to see which questions you got right and wrong and the rationales given. **NOTE: You will be able to access this link only immediately after you finish the test.**

Once you log out, you will be able to access your test results for 30 days by logging back in, but you will not be able to view the individual questions and their rationales.

APPENDIXES

■ APPENDIX A: THE CRNE COMPETENCIES

ASSUMPTIONS

Throughout the development of the CRNE competencies, the following assumptions were established:

1. The CRNE competencies are directed toward the professional practice of the entry-level registered nurse in Canada.

2. Entry-level registered nurses practise in a manner consistent with:

    (a) professional nursing practice standards of the regulatory body;

    (b) nursing codes of ethics;

    (c) scope of nursing practice applicable in the jurisdiction; and

    (d) common law and provincial/territorial and federal legislation that direct practice. (Jurisdictional Collaborative Process, 2006)

3. The CRNE competencies are each of equal importance for safe, ethical and effective practice of entry-level registered nurses.

4. The entry-level registered nurse is a generalist whose practice, autonomy and proficiency will be enhanced by reflective practice, evidence-informed knowledge, and collaboration and support from registered nurse colleagues, other health-care team members and employers.

5. The entry-level registered nurse is prepared to practise safely and competently along the continuum of care in situations of health and illness across a client's lifespan.

6. The entry-level registered nurse and the client[3] are partners in the decision-making process related to the client's health.

7. The CRNE competencies are grounded within the context of the client's health, the principles of primary health care, current and emerging health trends, determinants of health, the Canadian health-care system and professional nursing practice.

8. The practice environment of entry-level registered nurses can be any setting, program or circumstance in which nursing is practised (e.g., hospitals, communities, homes, clinics, schools, industries, residential facilities, telehealth, correctional facilities). (Jurisdictional Collaborative Process, 2006)

9. The nursing process is used by registered nurses to think critically and to make sound and reasonable decisions (Potter, Griffin Perry, Ross-Kerr, and Wood, 2006) and is reflected throughout the competencies.

10. The entry-level registered nurse has a leadership role in the health-care system. Leadership is not limited to formalized roles. (College of Registered Nurses of Nova Scotia, 2004; Jurisdictional Collaborative Process, 2006)

11. The entry-level registered nurse uses information and communication technologies to interpret, organize and utilize data to influence nursing practice, improve client outcomes and contribute to knowledge development in nursing. (Hebert, 2000)

---

[3] The term "client" refers to an individual, family, group, population or community.

1. PROFESSIONAL PRACTICE

Registered nursing competencies in this category focus on personal professional growth, as well as intraprofessional, interprofessional and intersectoral practice responsibilities. Each registered nurse is accountable for safe, compassionate, competent and ethical nursing practice. Professional practice occurs within the context of the *Code of Ethics for Registered Nurses* (CNA, 2008), provincial/territorial standards of practice and scope of practice, legislation and common law. Registered nurses are expected to demonstrate professional conduct as reflected by the attitudes, beliefs and values espoused in the *Code of Ethics for Registered Nurses.*

Professional registered nurse practice is self-regulating. Nursing practice requires professional judgment, interprofessional collaboration, leadership, management skills, cultural safety, advocacy, political awareness and social responsibility. Professional practice includes awareness of the need for, and the ability to ensure, continued professional development. This ability involves the capacity to perform self-assessments, seek feedback and plan self-directed learning activities that ensure professional growth. Registered nurses are expected to use knowledge and research to build an evidence-informed practice.

The registered nurse:

PP-1   practises in a manner consistent with the values in the *Code of Ethics for Registered Nurses* (e.g., providing safe, compassionate, competent and ethical care; promoting health and well-being; promoting and respecting informed decision-making; preserving dignity; maintaining privacy and confidentiality; promoting justice; being accountable). (CNA, 2008)

PP-2   practises in a manner that recognizes and respects the intrinsic worth of clients (e.g., providing privacy, respecting diversity and vulnerabilities, relieving suffering, respecting and fostering cultural expression, appropriately using chemical and physical restraints, accepting a client's report of pain). (CNA, 2008)

PP-3   applies ethical and legal principles related to maintaining client confidentiality in all forms of communication: written, oral and electronic (e.g., blogs, social networking sites, camera phones, text messaging, e-documentation, electronic health records). (Jurisdictional Collaborative Process, 2006)

PP-4   uses professional judgment when accessing, organizing and using electronic resources (e.g., for own professional development, nursing practice, text messaging, personal digital assistant).

PP-5   maintains clear, concise, accurate, objective and timely documentation.

PP-6   uses established communication protocols within and across health-care agencies and with other service sectors (e.g., preserving privacy, maintaining confidentiality, following appropriate channels of communication). (Jurisdictional Collaborative Process, 2006)

PP-7   advocates for equitable treatment and allocation of resources for the client (e.g., assisting vulnerable and marginalized clients to gain access to quality health care, facilitating and monitoring the quality of care, facilitating appropriate and timely responses by health-care team members, challenging questionable decisions).

PP-8   demonstrates accountability for own actions and decisions.

PP-9   practises within the scope of practice of the registered nurse.

PP-10 articulates the registered nurse's scope of practice to others (e.g., the client, health-care team members, the public, community leaders, politicians).

PP-11   provides rationale for nursing actions and decisions based on professional judgment and theoretical and evidence-informed knowledge from nursing and related disciplines.

PP-12   uses professional judgment when following agency policies, procedures and protocols (e.g., when to use chemical and physical restraints, when to consult another member of the health-care team).

PP-13   uses professional judgment in the absence of agency policies, procedures and protocols.

PP-14   integrates continuous quality improvement into nursing practice (e.g., identifying and reporting when a policy, procedure or protocol is unsafe, obsolete or unnecessary; participating in audits; participating in quality improvement committees). (Jurisdictional Collaborative Process, 2006)

PP-15   uses evidence and critical inquiry to challenge, change, enhance or support nursing practice (e.g., questioning accepted practice, participating in research).

PP-16   takes action when aware of potential or actual abuse of the client by health-care professionals, family or others.

PP-17   takes action when aware of potential or actual abusive situations to protect self and colleagues from injury (e.g., aggressive behaviours, bullying, workplace incivility, non-abuse policies). (Jurisdictional Collaborative Process, 2006)

PP-18   recognizes and reports errors, near misses and sentinel events and takes action to minimize harm (e.g., client incorrectly identified, error in drug administration).

PP-19   intervenes when unsafe practice of nursing colleagues and other members of the health-care team is identified (e.g., talking to colleague, stopping the unsafe practice, reporting to appropriate authority).

PP-20   uses conflict resolution strategies.

PP-21   implements strategies for continuing competence based on reflective practice, identified strengths, limitations and learning needs.

PP-22   is accountable when assigning nursing activities to other health-care providers consistent with competence, expertise, education, role description/agency policy, legislation and the client's needs (e.g., assessment, planning, implementation and evaluation of workload assignment).

PP-23   manages workloads effectively (e.g., time management, prioritizing, assignment).

PP-24   seeks appropriate assistance when unsafe workload is identified.

PP-25   collaborates and builds partnerships with nursing colleagues and other members of the health-care team to provide health services.

PP-26   understands the roles and contributions of other health-care team members (e.g., scope of practice, role description, consultation).

PP-27   shares knowledge and provides constructive feedback to colleagues (e.g., peer assessment, continuing competence, nursing students, mentorship, interprofessional rounds).

PP-28   manages resources in an effective and efficient manner (e.g., human, material, technological, financial).

2.   NURSE-CLIENT PARTNERSHIP

Registered nursing competencies in this category focus on therapeutic use of self, communication skills, nursing knowledge and collaboration to achieve the client's identified health goals. The nurse-client partnership is a purposeful, goal-directed relationship between nurse and client that is directed at advancing the best interest and health outcome of clients. The therapeutic partnership is central to all nursing practice and is grounded in an interpersonal process that occurs between the nurse and client (Registered Nurses' Association of Ontario, 2002). The registered nurse approaches this partnership with self-awareness, trust, respect, openness, empathy and sensitivity to diversity, reflecting the uniqueness of the client.

The registered nurse:

NCP-1   applies the principles of a therapeutic nurse-client relationship and responds appropriately (e.g., openness, non-judgmental attitude, active listening, self-awareness).

NCP-2   uses therapeutic verbal and non-verbal communication techniques with the client.

NCP-3   establishes a therapeutic relationship with the client (e.g., maintaining professionalism, maintaining boundaries).

NCP-4   fosters an environment that encourages questioning and exchange of information.

NCP-5   analyzes the impact of personal values and assumptions on interactions with clients (e.g., cultural safety, ethical issues).

NCP-6   applies principles of effective group processes (e.g., group roles, group phases, group dynamics, establishing group norms).

NCP-7   demonstrates sensitivity to and respect for diversity in health practices and beliefs (e.g., sexual orientation, gender identity, childbirth practices, dietary differences, gender, beliefs, values, spirituality, culture, language).

NCP-8   ensures that the client's informed consent has been obtained prior to providing nursing care, including involving others in the care (e.g., implied consent for nursing care).

NCP-9   supports the informed choice of the client in making decisions about care (e.g., right to refuse, right to request care, right to choose, right to participate in research).

NCP-10   facilitates and respects the client's informed choice to use alternative or complementary therapies (e.g., aromatherapy, acupressure, therapeutic touch, nutritional supplements, diets).

NCP-11   collaborates with clients in developing strategies to accommodate or modify health practices (e.g., integrating traditional food into a diabetic diet, modifying built environments, promoting healthy choices in schools).

NCP-12   provides care that is supportive to the client experiencing loss (e.g., loss of health, amputation, natural disaster, chronic illness, death).

NCP-13   promotes the client's positive self-concept (e.g., supporting cultural and spiritual preferences, validating the client's strengths, promoting the use of effective coping techniques, building community capacity).

NCP-14   uses principles/strategies related to teaching and learning to meet the client's learning needs (e.g., assessing readiness to learn, identifying strategies for change, establishing an environment conducive to learning, evaluating learning process, using theoretical approaches, using social marketing).

3. HEALTH AND WELLNESS

Registered nursing competencies in this category focus on recognizing and valuing health and wellness. The category encompasses the concept of population health and the principles of primary health care. Registered nurses partner with clients to develop personal skills, create supportive environments for health, strengthen community action, reorient health services and build healthy public policy. Nursing practice is influenced by continuing competency, determinants of health, life phases, demographics, health trends, economic and political factors, evidence-informed knowledge and research.

The registered nurse:

HW-1   collaborates with clients to identify priority areas for health promotion (e.g., healthy public policy, environmental health, stress management, social justice).

HW-2   assists clients in understanding links between health promotion strategies and health (e.g., education programs regarding cancer risks, health fairs, anti-smoking campaigns, handwashing campaigns, ergonomics).

HW-3   collaborates with key partners in health promotion activities (e.g., community leaders, public- and private-sector organizations, special interest groups).

HW-4   collaborates with clients to prioritize needs and develop prevention strategies (e.g., safe needle exchange, condoms in public places, reading nutritional labels).

HW-5   collaborates with clients and other health-care providers to respond to rapidly changing complex health risks (e.g., SARS outbreak, Norwalk virus, antibiotic-resistant organisms, pandemic).

HW-6   collaborates with clients to identify appropriate groups and resources for mutual aid, support and community action (e.g., poverty, homelessness, marginalized and vulnerable populations).

HW-7   collaborates with other health-care team members to implement strategies that prevent violence, abuse and neglect (e.g., using screening tools, providing information).

HW-8   collaborates with other health-care team members in implementing strategies related to the prevention and early detection of prevalent diseases (e.g., cardiovascular disease, cancer, diabetes, communicable disease).

HW-9   collaborates with other health-care team members in implementing strategies related to the prevention of addictive behaviours (e.g., smoking, substance use, gambling).

HW-10 collaborates with other health-care team members in implementing strategies to promote mental health (e.g., stress management, support groups, coping strategies, public policy, crisis intervention).

HW-11 coordinates activities with the client and others to facilitate continuity of care (e.g., cardiac rehabilitation, breastfeeding support, nutrition program).

HW-12 promotes and utilizes safety measures to prevent injury to clients (e.g., accessibility of a call bell, supervision, diffusion of potentially violent situations, suicide prevention, least restraint, falls prevention, seat belts, bicycle helmets, smoke alarms, infant car seats).

HW-13 promotes healthy lifestyle practices (e.g., physical activity and exercise, nutrition, rest/sleep, stress management, sexual health, family planning, contraception, hygiene, waste disposal, food preparation, infection prevention and control, smoking cessation, mental health).

HW-14   implements strategies related to the safe and appropriate use of medication (e.g., overuse or underuse of antibiotics, polypharmacy, complementary medicine, over-the-counter medication, medication reconciliation).

HW-15   takes action to address actual or potential risk factors related to health (e.g., food access, unsafe sexual practices, inactivity, smoking).

HW-16   takes action to address actual or potential environmental risk factors (e.g., incidents and accidents, environmental contaminants, mechanical equipment, infectious diseases).

HW-17   takes action to address actual or potential risks of abuse (e.g., intimate partner violence, older adult abuse, child abuse, sexual abuse, bullying, substance abuse, workplace incivility).

HW-18   participates in preventive strategies related to workplace safety (e.g., occupational health and safety practice, latex sensitivity protocols, needleless systems, musculoskeletal injury prevention, protective equipment, WHMIS, managing aggressive and violent behaviour, pandemic planning, healthy workplace environment initiative).

HW-19   incorporates determinants of health into the plan of care (e.g., adequate income, food and water safety, adequate housing and shelter).

HW-20   incorporates research about health risks and risk/harm reduction to support evidence-informed practice (e.g., second-hand smoke, Pap smears).

HW-21   uses the appropriate protocol when there is risk of communicable disease transmission (e.g., education on hand hygiene, isolation protocol, adhering to reporting protocols, encouraging needle exchange program, participating in immunization programs).

HW-22   supports the client in role change and/or developmental transitions (e.g., parenting groups, retirement, job loss, puberty, menopause).

HW-23   documents relevant data related to health promotion, risk reduction and injury and illness prevention (e.g., needs assessment, program planning, implementation, evaluation).

HW-24   uses safety measures to protect self, colleagues and clients from injury (e.g., non-scented products, harassment, psychological abuse, physical aggression, safe walking buddy system, falls prevention, workplace incivility).

HW-25   provides education about immunization programs.

HW-26   provides evidence-informed health-related information to clients (e.g., credible electronic sources, relevant and current information).

HW-27   uses data collection techniques that are appropriate to the client and the situation (e.g., community assessment, assessment tools).

4. CHANGES IN HEALTH

Registered nurse competencies in this category focus on care across the lifespan of the client who is experiencing changes in health. The competencies in this category thus focus on health promotion and illness prevention activities, as well as on acute, chronic, rehabilitative, palliative and end-of-life care. Such nursing actions may be delivered across a range of settings. Essential aspects of nursing care include critical inquiry, safety, solution-focused approaches, reflective practice and evidence-informed decision-making. Registered nurses collaborate with clients and other health-care professionals to identify health priorities and empower clients to improve their own health. In responding to and managing health situations, registered nurses promote optimal quality of life and development of self-care capacity and dignity during illness and during the dying and death process.

The registered nurse:

CH-1   collaborates with clients in a holistic assessment (e.g., physical, emotional, mental, spiritual, cognitive, developmental, environmental, meaning of health). (Jurisdictional Collaborative Process, 2006)

CH-2   involves clients in identifying their health needs, strengths, capacities and goals (e.g., the use of community development and empowerment principles, networking strategies, understanding of relational power, community capacity assessment).

CH-3   collects assessment data from a range of appropriate sources (e.g., the client, previous and current health records, nursing care plans, collaborative plans of care, family members, significant others, substitute decision-makers, census data, epidemiological data, evidence-informed data, referrals, other health-care providers).

CH-4   uses appropriate assessment techniques for data collection, (e.g., observation, inspection, auscultation, palpation, percussion, selected screening tests, pain scales, interview, consultation, focus group, measuring and monitoring).

CH-5   validates data collected with the client and appropriate sources (e.g., medication reconciliation, health history, consultations, referrals).

CH-6   analyzes data to establish relationships and draw conclusions from the various data collected (e.g., determining relationship between health assessment and laboratory values).

CH-7   applies knowledge from nursing and other disciplines concerning current health situations (e.g., the health-care needs of older adults, vulnerable and/or marginalized populations, health promotion and injury prevention, pain prevention and management, end-of-life care, addiction, blood-borne pathogens, traumatic stress syndrome). (Jurisdictional Collaborative Process, 2006)

CH-8   applies knowledge from the health sciences (e.g., physiology, pathophysiology, psychopathology, pharmacology, microbiology, epidemiology, genetics, immunology, nutrition, sociology). (Jurisdictional Collaborative Process, 2006)

CH-9   identifies actual and potential changes in health (e.g., pain management, disability, immobility).

CH-10 collaborates with the client in developing and implementing the plan of care (e.g., setting priorities, establishing target dates, selecting relevant interventions, developing teaching plans, administration of insulin, home IV and TPN programs, referring to self-care groups).

CH-11 incorporates the client's personal strengths and resources in meeting self-care needs (e.g., healthy habits, personal beliefs, complementary and alternative therapies, social supports, coping strategies).

CH-12   uses evidence-informed knowledge to assist the client to understand interventions and their relationship to expected outcomes (e.g., possible risks and benefits, discomforts, inconveniences, costs).

CH-13   individualizes the plan of care to apply interventions consistent with the client's capacities, identified priorities and health situation (e.g., geriatric care, palliative care).

CH-14   collaborates with the client during the care process to prepare for transfer and discharge (e.g., discharge teaching and planning, transfer of care).

CH-15   documents nursing practice (e.g., assessment data, written plan, actual care, evaluation).

CH-16   applies technology in accordance with available resources and the client's needs (e.g., relevant web-based material, e-documentation, telehealth, patient lifts, home IV pumps).

CH-17   supports the client through transitions related to health situations (e.g., new diagnoses, chronic illness, dying process).

CH-18   facilitates physical, psychological and psychosocial adjustment (e.g., therapeutic communication, counselling, appropriate referral, chronic disease management).

CH-19   facilitates the involvement of family and significant others in collaboration with the client.

CH-20   prevents and minimizes complications (e.g., turning and positioning, early detection and intervention).

CH-21   evaluates changes in the client's health status (e.g., decreased oxygen saturation, decreased urine output).

CH-22   manages multiple nursing interventions simultaneously (e.g., prioritizing and organizing interventions).

CH-23   communicates accurate and relevant information about the client's health situation to appropriate health-care team members.

CH-24   intervenes in a timely manner to changes observed in the client's health situation.

CH-25   evaluates the effectiveness of nursing interventions in collaboration with the client (e.g., learning needs, comparing actual outcomes to anticipated outcomes).

CH-26   modifies plan of care based on an ongoing holistic assessment of the client's changing health situation.

CH-27   initiates urgent inclusion of the health-care team members in response to the client's changing health status (e.g., hemorrhage, imminent birth, low blood pressure, drug reactions).

CH-28   coordinates activities with the client and other members of the health-care team to promote continuity and consistency of care within and across settings (e.g., referrals, unit reports, community health centres, air and ground transport).

CH-29   consults with other health-care team members to analyze and plan care in complex health situations (e.g., obesity, comorbidities, chemical exposure, burns, cancer, complex family situations). (Jurisdictional Collaborative Process, 2006)

CH-30   prepares the client for diagnostic procedures and treatments (e.g., explanation, evidence-informed information, tests, obtaining specimens).

CH-31   provides preoperative and postoperative care.

CH-32   promotes oxygenation (e.g., positioning, deep breathing and coughing exercises, oxygen therapy, oral and nasal suctioning).

CH-33   promotes circulation (e.g., active or passive exercises, positioning, mobilization, cast care).

CH-34   promotes and monitors fluid balance (e.g., intake and output, weight, non-invasive hemodynamic measurement, measuring abdominal girth).

CH-35   promotes and manages adequate nutrition (e.g., burns, inflammatory bowel disease, diabetes, HIV/AIDS, infant gastric reflux, obesity, malnutrition).

CH-36   administers and manages parenteral and enteral nutrition (e.g., TPN, nasogastric tube).

CH-37   promotes and manages adequate urinary elimination (e.g., stoma care, bladder retraining, self-catheterization, bladder irrigation, bladder catheterization, pharmacological measures).

CH-38   promotes and manages adequate bowel elimination (e.g., bowel retraining, ostomy care, enema, rectal tubes, pharmacological measures, dietary measures).

CH-39   promotes and ensures a client's proper body alignment (e.g., proper positioning, external immobilizing devices).

CH-40   promotes mobility (e.g., active and passive exercises, early ambulation, activities of daily living, prosthetic and mobilizing devices, use of ergonomics).

CH-41   promotes and maintains tissue integrity (e.g., providing skin and wound care).

CH-42   promotes and maintains comfort (e.g., the nurse's presence, warm and cold application, touch, positioning).

CH-43   determines and implements appropriate sensory stimulation for the client's health situation (e.g., touch with unconscious client, minimizing environmental stimuli, sensory stimulation for premature infant in isolette, adolescent in isolation).

CH-44   evaluates safe use of prescribed and non-prescribed medication (e.g., safe dosage and route, food-drug interactions, drug-drug interactions, age, weight).

CH-45   takes action with unsafe medication packaging and/or orders.

CH-46   calculates medication dosage.

CH-47   administers medication (e.g., right client, drug, dose, route and time; documentation; client's rights; right reason; allergies).

CH-48   evaluates client's response to medication (e.g., desired effects, adverse effects, interactions).

CH-49   assesses when a p.r.n. medication is indicated (e.g., analgesics, inhalers, antihypertensives, antianginals, laxatives, antianxiety agents).

CH-50   takes action when desired responses to medication are not attained.

CH-51   assists the client to manage pain with non-pharmacological measures (e.g., applying heat and cold, touch, massage, visual imagery, turning and positioning).

CH-52   assists the client to manage pain with pharmacological agents or devices (e.g., non-opiates, opiates, epidural analgesia, patient-controlled analgesia [PCA]).

CH-53   collects and communicates accurate medication information (e.g., medication reconciliation upon admission, at transfer of care, at discharge).

CH-54   administers blood and blood products safely.

CH-55   manages central venous access devices (e.g., implanted devices, PICC lines, infusion pumps).

CH-56   manages drainage tubes and collection devices (e.g., chest tubes and vacuum drainages).

CH-57   inserts, maintains and removes nasogastric tubes.

CH-58   inserts, maintains and removes peripheral intravenous therapy.

CH-59   applies routine/standard precautions.

CH-60   intervenes in a rapidly changing health situation: acute cardiovascular event (e.g., myocardial infarction, unstable angina).

CH-61   intervenes in a rapidly changing health situation: acute neurological event (e.g., brain attack [stroke], trans-ischemic attack [TIA], seizure, head injury).

CH-62   intervenes in a rapidly changing health situation: shock (e.g., hypovolemic, anaphylactic, neurogenic, cardiogenic, septic and hemodynamic deterioration).

CH-63   intervenes in a rapidly changing health situation: acute respiratory event (e.g., acute asthma, pulmonary embolus, pulmonary edema).

CH-64   intervenes in a rapidly changing health situation: cardiopulmonary arrest.

CH-65   intervenes in a rapidly changing health situation: perinatal (antepartum, intrapartum, postpartum, newborn).

CH-66   intervenes in a rapidly changing health situation: diabetes crisis (e.g., diabetic coma, hyperglycemia, hypoglycemia, ketoacidosis).

CH-67   intervenes in a rapidly changing health situation: mental health crisis (e.g., psychotic episode, neuroleptic malignant syndrome, suicide ideation, delirium, acute onset of extrapyramidal side-effects).

CH-68   intervenes in a rapidly changing health situation: trauma (e.g., burns, fractures).

CH-69   intervenes in a rapidly changing health situation: postoperatively (e.g., malignant hyperthermia, hemorrhage, wound dehiscence).

CH-70   intervenes in a rapidly changing health situation: acute renal failure (e.g., nephrotoxins).

CH-71   provides supportive care to meet hospice, palliative or end-of-life care needs of dying clients (e.g., symptom control, spiritual care, advocacy, family counselling, support for clients and significant others, advance care planning, grief and bereavement counselling). (Jurisdictional Collaborative Process, 2006)

CH-72   intervenes to meet spiritual needs (e.g., assessing for spiritual distress, providing time for prayer or meditation, appropriate referral, cultural safety).

CH-73   facilitates with the client to explore and access community resources (e.g., self-help groups, geriatric day programs, respite care, finances, transportation, social networks).

CH-74   facilitates the client's development of independence and safety in activities of daily living (e.g., removal of scatter rugs, keeping essential furniture on one level of the house, raised toilet seat, ordering specialized equipment such as a walker and special utensils, consulting with other health-care team members).

CH-75   facilitates social well-being of the client (e.g., encouraging and creating opportunities for social participation, encouraging development of new interests and support systems, facilitating peer-to-peer helping model).

CH-76   facilitates the client's reintegration into family and community networks (e.g., adaptation to role transitions, physical mobility, self-help groups).

CH-77   provides supportive care to clients with chronic health situations (e.g., outpatient clinics, adult day care, respite care, pain management, symptom management, polypharmacy, group therapy, addictions counselling).

CH-78   demonstrates understanding of organizational responses and appropriate nursing roles in emergency community disasters and emerging global health issues (e.g., mass casualty response, bioterrorism, pandemic, emergency preparedness/disaster planning, food and water safety).

CH-79   takes appropriate nursing actions in disaster situations (e.g., mass casualty response, bioterrorism).

■ APPENDIX B: ABBREVIATIONS

These abbreviations are acceptable for use on the Canadian Registered Nurse Examination:

b.i.d.	–	twice daily	min	–	minute(s)
BP	–	blood pressure	mL	–	millilitre(s)
°C	–	degrees Celsius	mmHg	–	millimetres mercury
cm	–	centimetre(s)	mmol	–	millimole(s)
g	–	gram(s)	mmol/L	–	millimoles per litre
gtt	–	drops	P	–	pulse
h	–	hour	p.o.	–	orally
HR	–	heart rate (beats/min)	p.r.n.	–	as needed
IM	–	intramuscular	q.i.d.	–	4 times daily
IV	–	intravenous	q.8h	–	every 8 hours
kg	–	kilogram(s)	RR	–	respirations
L	–	litre(s)	stat.	–	immediately
mEq	–	milliequivalent	T	–	temperature
mg	–	milligram(s)	t.i.d.	–	3 times daily

ADDITIONAL MATERIALS

■ ADDITIONAL MATERIALS

PERFORMANCE PROFILE TALLY SHEET

Table 1: 1st Writing

Competency Category

CATEGORY	TOTAL INCORRECT		TOTAL IN CATEGORIES		% INCORRECT	
Professional Practice		÷	34	x	100 =	%
Nurse-Client Partnership		÷	23	x	100 =	%
Health and Wellness		÷	47	x	100 =	%
Changes in Health		÷	96	x	100 =	%
Total Incorrect		÷	**200**	x	**100 =**	%

Taxonomy Levels of Cognitive Ability

CATEGORY	TOTAL INCORRECT		TOTAL IN CATEGORIES		% INCORRECT	
Knowledge/Comprehension		÷	30	x	100 =	%
Application		÷	88	x	100 =	%
Critical Thinking		÷	82	x	100 =	%
Total Incorrect		÷	**200**	x	**100 =**	%

Table 2: 2nd Writing

Competency Category

CATEGORY	TOTAL INCORRECT		TOTAL IN CATEGORIES		% INCORRECT	
Professional Practice		÷	34	x	100 =	%
Nurse-Client Partnership		÷	23	x	100 =	%
Health and Wellness		÷	47	x	100 =	%
Changes in Health		÷	96	x	100 =	%
Total Incorrect		÷	**200**	**x**	**100 =**	%

Taxonomy Levels of Cognitive Ability

CATEGORY	TOTAL INCORRECT		TOTAL IN CATEGORIES		% INCORRECT	
Knowledge/Comprehension		÷	30	x	100 =	%
Application		÷	88	x	100 =	%
Critical Thinking		÷	82	x	100 =	%
Total Incorrect		÷	**200**	**x**	**100 =**	%

Table 3: 3rd Writing

Competency Category

CATEGORY	TOTAL INCORRECT		TOTAL IN CATEGORIES		% INCORRECT	
Professional Practice		÷	34	x	100 =	%
Nurse-Client Partnership		÷	23	x	100 =	%
Health and Wellness		÷	47	x	100 =	%
Changes in Health		÷	96	x	100 =	%
Total Incorrect		÷	**200**	x	**100 =**	%

Taxonomy Levels of Cognitive Ability

CATEGORY	TOTAL INCORRECT		TOTAL IN CATEGORIES		% INCORRECT	
Knowledge/Comprehension		÷	30	x	100 =	%
Application		÷	88	x	100 =	%
Critical Thinking		÷	82	x	100 =	%
Total Incorrect		÷	**200**	x	**100 =**	%

PERFORMANCE PROFILE CHART

Table 1: 1st Writing

Competency Category

% OF INCORRECT ANSWERS

%	0	5	10	15	20	25	30	35	40	45	50	55	60	65	70	75	80	85	90	95
PP																				
NCP																				
HW																				
CH																				

COMPETENCY CATEGORIES

PP	–	Professional Practice
NCP	–	Nurse-Client Partnership
HW	–	Health and Wellness
CH	–	Changes in Health

Taxonomy Levels of Cognitive Ability

% OF INCORRECT ANSWERS

%	0	5	10	15	20	25	30	35	40	45	50	55	60	65	70	75	80	85	90	95
K/C																				
APP																				
CT																				

TAXONOMY OF COGNITIVE ABILITY

K/C	–	Knowledge/Comprehension
APP	–	Application
CT	–	Critical Thinking

Table 2: 2nd Writing

Competency Category

% OF INCORRECT ANSWERS

%	0	5	10	15	20	25	30	35	40	45	50	55	60	65	70	75	80	85	90	95
PP																				
NCP																				
HW																				
CH																				

COMPETENCY CATEGORIES

PP	–	Professional Practice
NCP	–	Nurse-Client Partnership
HW	–	Health and Wellness
CH	–	Changes in Health

Taxonomy Levels of Cognitive Ability

% OF INCORRECT ANSWERS

%	0	5	10	15	20	25	30	35	40	45	50	55	60	65	70	75	80	85	90	95
K/C																				
APP																				
CT																				

TAXONOMY OF COGNITIVE ABILITY

K/C	–	Knowledge/Comprehension
APP	–	Application
CT	–	Critical Thinking

Table 3: 3rd Writing

Competency Category

% OF INCORRECT ANSWERS

%	0	5	10	15	20	25	30	35	40	45	50	55	60	65	70	75	80	85	90	95
PP																				
NCP																					
HW																					
CH																					

COMPETENCY CATEGORIES

PP – Professional Practice
NCP – Nurse-Client Partnership
HW – Health and Wellness
CH – Changes in Health

Taxonomy of Cognitive Ability Levels

% OF INCORRECT ANSWERS

%	0	5	10	15	20	25	30	35	40	45	50	55	60	65	70	75	80	85	90	95
K/C																					
APP																					
CT																					

TAXONOMY OF COGNITIVE ABILITY

K/C – Knowledge/Comprehension
APP – Application
CT – Critical Thinking

ANSWER SHEETS

ANSWER SHEET
(See instructions on reverse)

FEUILLE-RÉPONSES
(Voir les instructions au verso)

Family Name - Nom de famille | First Name - Prénom

Date of Birth - Date de naissance | Date of Writing - Date de l'examen

/ / DY - JR   MO   YR - AN

/ / DY - JR   MO   YR - AN

Test - Examen

Language of Writing – Langue

English ○   Français ○

Place CANDIDATE LABEL here.

Apposer l'AUTOCOLLANT DU CANDIDAT ici.

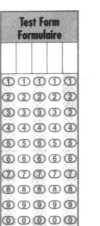

Print the test form number from the test booklet and fill in the corresponding ovals

Inscrivez le numéro du formulaire qui apparaît sur le cahier d'examen et noircissez les ovales correspondants

Test Form Formulaire

Candidate Number Numéro d'identité

Writing Centre Code Code du centre

SI/SEI   10.97

DesignExpert™ by NCS Mark Reflex® MM203508-2   65432   HR04

INSTRUCTIONS

- Use a #2 HB pencil.

- Do NOT use ink or ballpoint pens.

- Completely fill the ovals.

- Utilisez un crayon HB #2.

- Ne PAS utiliser de stylo.

- Noircissez les ovales complètement.

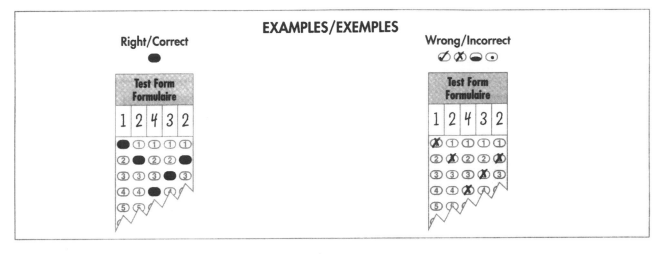

- Completely erase any answer you wish to change.

- Do NOT make any stray marks on the answer sheet.

- Do not fold or staple the answer sheet.

- Effacez complètement les réponses que vous voulez changer.

- Ne faites AUCUNE autre marque sur la feuille-réponses.

- Ne pas plier ou agrafer la feuille-réponses.

COMPLETE THE IDENTIFICATION PORTION OF YOUR ANSWER SHEET

- Print your name, date of birth, date of the examination and name of the examination (from the cover of your test booklet).

- Print the test form number from the test booklet and fill in the corresponding ovals.

REMPLISSEZ LA PARTIE RENSEIGNEMENTS DE VOTRE FEUILLE-RÉPONSES

- Inscrivez votre nom, votre date de naissance, la date de l'examen et le nom de l'examen (apparaissant sur la page couverture de votre cahier d'examen).

- Inscrivez le numéro du formulaire qui apparaît sur le cahier d'examen et noircissez les ovales correspondants.

If you have a candidate label:
- Detach candidate label from your identification card.
- Place the candidate label on the answer sheet.
- Do not fill in the information to the right of the candidate label unless the candidate label is incorrect.

If you do not have a candidate label:
- Fill the oval corresponding to the language of writing.
- Print, in the appropriate boxes, your candidate number and writing centre code. Fill in the corresponding oval for each digit.

Si vous avez un autocollant:
- Détachez l'autocollant de votre carte d'identité.
- Apposez l'autocollant dans l'espace réservé à cette fin sur la feuille-réponses.
- Ne pas remplir l'information à la droite de l'autocollant à moins que l'autocollant soit incorrect.

Si vous n'avez pas d'autocollant:
- Noircissez l'ovale correspondant à la langue de l'examen.
- Inscrivez, dans les espaces appropriés, le numéro d'identité et le code du centre d'examen. Noircissez l'ovale correspondant à chaque chiffre.

Please return to/Veuillez retourner à: ASI/SEI, 50 Driveway, Ottawa, ON K2P 1E2 1-613-237-9874

ANSWER SHEET
(See instructions on reverse)

FEUILLE-RÉPONSES
(Voir les instructions au verso)

Family Name - Nom de famille | First Name - Prénom

Date of Birth - Date de naissance | Date of Writing - Date de l'examen

/ / DY - JR   MO   YR - AN

/ / DY - JR   MO   YR - AN

Test - Examen

Place CANDIDATE LABEL here.

Apposer l'AUTOCOLLANT DU CANDIDAT ici.

Do not fill the information in this box unless you are missing a candidate label or the candidate label is incorrect.

Ne remplissez pas l'information de cette boîte sauf si vous n'avez pas d'autocollant ou si l'autocollant est incorrect.

Language of Writing – Langue	
English ○	Français ○

Print the test form number from the test booklet and fill in the corresponding ovals

Inscrivez le numéro du formulaire qui apparaît sur le cahier d'examen et noircissez les ovales correspondants

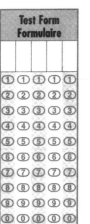

Test Form / Formulaire

Candidate Number / Numéro d'identité

Writing Centre Code / Code du centre

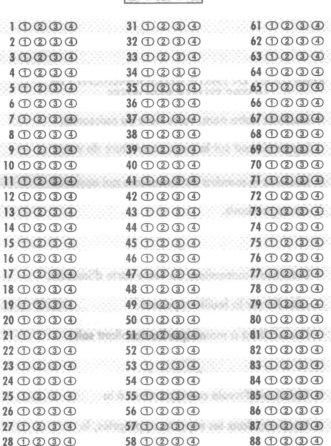

INSTRUCTIONS

- Use a #2 HB pencil.

- Do NOT use ink or ballpoint pens.

- Completely fill the ovals.

- Utilisez un crayon HB #2.

- Ne PAS utiliser de stylo.

- Noircissez les ovales complètement.

EXAMPLES/EXEMPLES

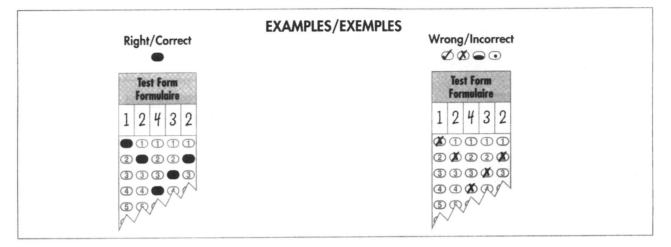

Right/Correct

Wrong/Incorrect

- Completely erase any answer you wish to change.

- Do NOT make any stray marks on the answer sheet.

- Do not fold or staple the answer sheet.

- Effacez complètement les réponses que vous voulez changer.

- Ne faites AUCUNE autre marque sur la feuille-réponses.

- Ne pas plier ou agrafer la feuille-réponses.

COMPLETE THE IDENTIFICATION PORTION OF YOUR ANSWER SHEET

- Print your name, date of birth, date of the examination and name of the examination (from the cover of your test booklet).

- Print the test form number from the test booklet and fill in the corresponding ovals.

If you have a candidate label:
- Detach candidate label from your identification card.
- Place the candidate label on the answer sheet.
- Do not fill in the information to the right of the candidate label unless the candidate label is incorrect.

If you do not have a candidate label:
- Fill the oval corresponding to the language of writing.
- Print, in the appropriate boxes, your candidate number and writing centre code. Fill in the corresponding oval for each digit.

REMPLISSEZ LA PARTIE RENSEIGNEMENTS DE VOTRE FEUILLE-RÉPONSES

- Inscrivez votre nom, votre date de naissance, la date de l'examen et le nom de l'examen (apparaissant sur la page couverture de votre cahier d'examen).

- Inscrivez le numéro du formulaire qui apparaît sur le cahier d'examen et noircissez les ovales correspondants.

Si vous avez un autocollant:
- Détachez l'autocollant de votre carte d'identité.
- Apposez l'autocollant dans l'espace réservé à cette fin sur la feuille-réponses.
- Ne pas remplir l'information à la droite de l'autocollant à moins que l'autocollant soit incorrect.

Si vous n'avez pas d'autocollant:
- Noircissez l'ovale correspondant à la langue de l'examen.
- Inscrivez, dans les espaces appropriés, le numéro d'identité et le code du centre d'examen. Noircissez l'ovale correspondant à chaque chiffre.

SATISFACTION SURVEY

■ SATISFACTION SURVEY – CRNE PREP GUIDE

Canadian Nurses Association – www.cna-aiic.ca

Your opinion is important to help us improve future editions of the *Canadian Registered Nurse Examination Prep Guide* and to better meet the needs of CRNE writers. Please complete the following satisfaction survey and mail or fax it to the Canadian Nurses Association (see address and fax number at the end of the survey). You can also complete this survey online using the link on the CD-ROM. Your responses will be treated with complete confidentiality. Please fill in the circle corresponding to your response.

A. *CRNE PREP GUIDE* CONTENT

Please rate the following aspects of the prep guide content:

		EXCELLENT	GOOD	AVERAGE	FAIR	POOR	N/A
1.	Background on the CRNE	○	○	○	○	○	○
2.	Overall content of the prep guide	○	○	○	○	○	○
3.	Overall size and length	○	○	○	○	○	○
4.	Organization/layout	○	○	○	○	○	○
5.	Test-taking strategies	○	○	○	○	○	○
6.	Overall usefulness in helping you prepare for the CRNE	○	○	○	○	○	○

B. *CRNE PREP GUIDE* USE

7. Did you complete the prep guide questions?
   ○ No – Please go to Section B (Q 15).
   ○ Yes – Please continue to Q 8.

8. By which method?
   ○ Paper version
   ○ CD-ROM
   ○ Both

Please rate the following aspects of the prep guide practice questions:

	EXCELLENT	GOOD	AVERAGE	FAIR	POOR	N/A
9. Overall rating of practice questions	O	O	O	O	O	O
10. Score interpretation of the practice questions	O	O	O	O	O	O
11. Performance profile	O	O	O	O	O	O
12. Answer rationales	O	O	O	O	O	O
13. Classification of questions (in rationales and performance profile)	O	O	O	O	O	O
14. References	O	O	O	O	O	O

C.   USE OF *CRNE PREP GUIDE* CD-ROM

15. Did you use the CD-ROM?
   O No – *Please go to Section C (Q 24).*
   O Yes – *Please continue to Q 16.*

Please rate the following aspects of the CD-ROM:

	EXCELLENT	GOOD	AVERAGE	FAIR	POOR	N/A
16. Overall rating of CD-ROM	O	O	O	O	O	O
17. Ease of use	O	O	O	O	O	O
18. Colour/graphics	O	O	O	O	O	O
19. Option to select a subset of questions (by type or competency category)	O	O	O	O	O	O
20. Option to exit test and resume an existing test session later	O	O	O	O	O	O
21. Option to save results to a file	O	O	O	O	O	O
22. Option to print results	O	O	O	O	O	O
23. Option to transfer your answers from paper version to create performance profile	O	O	O	O	O	O

D. *CRNE PREP GUIDE* **MARKETING**

24. How did you hear about the prep guide?
    - ○ Poster/advertisement
    - ○ Other student
    - ○ Brochure
    - ○ Conference
    - ○ Nursing instructor
    - ○ Website
    - ○ Other: _____

25. Did you take the CRNE Readiness Test?
    - ○ No
    - ○ Yes

26. Did you use any other exam practice book(s) in addition to the *CRNE Prep Guide*?
    - ○ No – *Please go to Q 28.*
    - ○ Yes – *Please continue to Q 27.*

27. Which did you prefer?
    - ○ *CRNE Prep Guide*
    - ○ Other, please specify _____

28. Who are you?
    - ○ Canadian-educated student/new grad
    - ○ Internationally educated nurse
    - ○ Nursing educator/instructor/professor
    - ○ Other, please specify _____

E. GENERAL COMMENTS

Thank you for completing this survey.

Please send this completed survey by mail to:
Canadian Nurses Association, 50 Driveway, Ottawa, ON K2P 1E2

by fax to: 613-237-3520

or complete the survey online at www.cna-aiic.ca

Please note that the CD-ROM version includes a link to the satisfaction survey.
If you wish to test yourself with a different sample of questions, visit the CRNE Readiness Test web page
on the CNA website at http://readiness.ca-aiic.ca

BIBLIOGRAPHY

BIBLIOGRAPHY

NOTE: The references in bold are recommended by the content experts as the ones most commonly used and frequently referenced for introductory nursing practice.

Abrams, A. C., Pennington, S. S., & Lammon, B. (2007). *Clinical drug therapy: Rationales for nursing practice* (8th ed.). Philadelphia: Lippincott Williams & Wilkins.

Ackley, B. J., & Ladwig, G. B. (2006). *Nursing diagnosis handbook: A guide to planning care* (7th ed.). St. Louis: Mosby.

Allender, J. A., & Walton Spradley, B. (2005). *Community health nursing: Promoting and protecting the public's health* (6th ed.). Philadelphia: Lippincott Williams & Wilkins.

Arnold, E. C., & Underman Boggs, K. (2007). *Interpersonal relationships: Professional communication skills for nurses* (5th ed.). St. Louis: Elsevier Saunders.

Austin, W., & Boyd, M. A. (2008). *Psychiatric nursing for Canadian practice*. Philadelphia: Lippincott Williams & Wilkins.

Bastable, S. (2008). *Nurse as educator: Principles of teaching and learning for nursing practice* (3rd ed.). Boston: Jones & Bartlett.

Black, J. M., & Hokanson Hawks, J. (2005). *Medical-surgical nursing: Clinical management for positive outcomes* (7th ed.). St. Louis: Elsevier Saunders.

Black, J. M., & Hokanson Hawks, J. (2009). *Medical-surgical nursing: Clinical management for positive outcomes* (8th ed.). St. Louis: Elsevier Saunders.

Bloom, B. S. (Ed.) (1956). *Taxonomy of educational objectives, handbook I: The cognitive domain*. New York: David McKay Company, Inc.

Brophy, K. M., Scarlett-Ferguson, H., & Webber, K. S. (2008). *Clinical drug therapy for Canadian practice* (1st Canadian ed.). Philadelphia: Lippincott Williams & Wilkins.

Burns, C. E., Dunn, A. M., Brady, M. A., Barber Starr, N., & Blosser, C. G. (2009). *Pediatric primary care* (4th ed.). St. Louis: Elsevier Saunders.

Canadian Nurses Association. (2004). *Everyday ethics: Putting the code into practice*. Ottawa: Author.

Canadian Nurses Association. (2008). *Code of ethics for registered nurses*. Ottawa: Author.

Canadian Pharmacists Association. (2008). *Compendium of pharmaceuticals and specialties 2008: The Canadian drug reference for health professionals*. Ottawa: Author.

Carpenito-Moyet, L. J. (2008). *Nursing diagnosis: Application to clinical practice* (12th ed.). Philadelphia: Lippincott Williams & Wilkins.

Cherry, B., & Jacob, S. R. (2008). *Contemporary nursing: Issues, trends and management* (4th ed.). St. Louis: Elsevier.

Clayton, B. D., Stock, Y. N., & Harroun, R. D. (2007). *Basic pharmacology for nurses* (14th ed.). St. Louis: Elsevier.

College of Registered Nurses of Nova Scotia. (2004). *Entry-level competencies for registered nurses in Nova Scotia*. Halifax: Author.

Community and Hospital Infection Control Association – Canada. (2008). *Information about hand hygiene*. Retrieved December 8, 2008, from http://www.chica.org/links_handhygiene.html#STANDARDS

Craven, R. F., & Hirnle, C. J. (2009). *Fundamentals of nursing: Human health and function* (6th ed.). Philadelphia: Lippincott Williams & Wilkins.

Day, R. A., Paul, P., Williams, B., Smeltzer, S. C., & Bare, B. (2007). *Brunner and Suddarth's textbook of medical-surgical nursing*. (1st Canadian ed.). Philadelphia: Lippincott Williams & Wilkins.

Donovan Monahan, F., Sands, J. K., Neighbors, M., Marek, J. F., & Green-Nigro, C. J. (2007). *Phipps' medical-surgical nursing: Health and illness perspective* (8th ed.). St. Louis: Elsevier

Ebersole, P., Hess, P., Touhy, T., Jett, K., & Luggen, A. (2008). *Toward healthy aging* (7th ed.). St. Louis: Elsevier.

Elkin, M. K., Griffin Perry, A., & Potter, P. A. (2007). *Nursing interventions and clinical skills* (4th ed.). St. Louis: Elsevier Health Sciences.

Emergency Nurses Association. (2005). *Sheehy's manual of emergency care* (6th ed.). St. Louis: Elsevier Mosby.

Evans, R. J., Evans, M. K., Brown, Y. M. R., & Orshan S. A. (2009). *Canadian maternity: Newborn and women's health nursing* (1st Canadian ed.). Philadelphia: Lippincott Williams & Wilkins.

Ferrell, B. R., & Coyle, N. (2006). *Textbook of palliative nursing* (2nd ed.). New York: Oxford University Press, Inc.

Fortinash, K. M., & Holoday Worret, P. A. (2008). *Psychiatric mental health nursing* (4th ed.). St. Louis: Mosby.

Gottlieb, L. N., & Feeley, N. (2006). *The collaborative partnership approach to care: A delicate balance.* Toronto: Mosby.

Griffin Perry, A., & Potter, P. A. (2006). *Clinical nursing skills & techniques* (6th ed.). St. Louis: Elsevier.

Hebert, M. (2000). A national education strategy to develop nursing informatics competencies. *Nursing Leadership (CJNL), 13*(2), 11-14.

Hibberd, J. M., & Smith, D. L. (2006). *Nursing leadership and management in Canada* (3rd ed.). Toronto: Elsevier.

Hockenberry, M. J. (2005). *Wong's essentials of pediatric nursing* (7th ed.). St. Louis: Elsevier Mosby.

Hockenberry, M. J., & Wilson, D. (2007). *Wong's nursing care of infants and children* (8th ed.). St. Louis: Elsevier Mosby.

Hockenberry, M. J., & Wilson, D. (2009). *Wong's essentials of pediatric nursing* (8th ed.). St. Louis: Elsevier.

Hoffman Wold, G. (2008). *Basic geriatric nursing* (4th ed.). St. Louis: Elsevier.

Hopkins, T., & Myers, E. (2008). *MedSurg notes: Nurse's clinical pocket guide* (2nd ed.). Philadelphia: F. A. Davis Company.

Hopper Deglin, J., & Hazard Vallerand, A. (2006). *Davis's drug guide for nurses* (9th ed.). Philadelphia: F. A. Davis Company.

Huber, D. (2006). *Leadership and nursing care management* (3rd ed.). St. Louis: Elsevier.

Ignatavicius, D. D., & Workman, M. L. (2006). *Medical-surgical nursing: Critical thinking for collaborative care* (5th ed.). St. Louis: Elsevier.

James, S. R., & Ashwill, J. W. (2007). *Nursing care of children: Principles and practice* (3rd ed.). St. Louis: Elsevier Saunders.

Jurisdictional Collaborative Process. (2006). *A report of the 2004-2006 jurisdictional competency project: Competencies in the context of entry-level registered nurse practice.* Vancouver: College of Registered Nurses of British Columbia.

Karch, A. M. (2008). *2008 Lippincott's nursing drug guide.* Philadelphia: Lippincott Williams & Wilkins.

Keltner, N. L., Bostrom, C. E., & Hilyard Schwecke, L. (2007). *Psychiatric nursing* (5th ed.). St. Louis: Mosby.

Kittrell Chitty, K., & Perry Black, B. (2007). *Professional nursing: Concepts and challenges.* St. Louis: Elsevier Mosby.

Kuhn Timby, B., & Smith, N. E. (2007). *Introductory medical-surgical nursing* (9th ed.). Philadelphia: Lippincott Williams & Wilkins.

Kyle, T. (2008). *Essentials of pediatric nursing.* Philadelphia: Lippincott Williams & Wilkins.

Leeseberg Stamler, L., & Yiu, L. (2008). *Community health nursing: A Canadian perspective* (2nd ed.). Toronto: Pearson Education Canada.

Lehne, R. A. (2007). *Pharmacology for nursing care* (6th ed.). St. Louis: Elsevier Saunders.

Leifer, G. (2007). *Introduction to maternity and pediatric nursing* (5th ed.). St. Louis: Elsevier.

Leonard Lowdermilk, D., & Perry, E. S. (2006). *Maternity nursing* (7th ed.). St. Louis: Elsevier Mosby.

Leonard Lowdermilk, D., & Perry, E. S. (2007). *Maternity and women's health care* (9th ed.). St. Louis: Mosby.

Lilley, L. L., Harrington, S., Snyder, J. S., & Swart, B. (2007). *Pharmacology and the nursing process in Canada.* St. Louis: Elsevier Mosby.

Lium Edelman, C., & Mandle, C. L. (2006). *Health promotion throughout the life span* (6th ed). St. Louis: Elsevier Mosby.

Mantik Lewis, S., McLean Heitkemper, M., Ruff Dirksen, S., Goldsworthy, S., & Barry, M. A. (2006). *Medical-surgical nursing in Canada: Assessment and management of clinical problems* (1st Canadian ed.). Toronto: Mosby.

Mantik Lewis, S., McLean Heitkemper, M., Ruff Dirksen, S., Graber O'Brien, P., & Bucher, L. (2007). *Medical-surgical nursing: Assessment and management of clinical problems* (7th ed.). St. Louis: Mosby.

Marquis, B. L., & Huston, C. J. (2009). *Leadership roles and management functions in nursing: Theory and application* (6th ed.). Philadelphia: Wolters Kluwer Health.

Marriner-Tomey, A. (2008). *Guide to nursing management and leadership* (8th ed.). St. Louis: Elsevier.

Mason, D. J., Leavitt, J. K., & Chaffie, M. W. (2007). *Policies and politics in nursing and health care* (5th ed.). St. Louis: Elsevier.

Mattson Porth, C. (2006). *Essentials of pathophysiology: Concepts of altered health states* (2nd ed.). Philadelphia: Lippincott Williams & Wilkins.

Maurer, F. A., & Smith, C. (2005). *Community/Public health nursing practice* (3rd ed.). St. Louis: Elsevier.

Maurer, F. A., & Smith, C. (2009). *Community/Public health nursing practice: Health for families and populations.* St. Louis: Elsevier.

Meiner, S. E., & Lueckenotte, A. G. (2006). *Gerontologic nursing* (3rd ed.). St. Louis: Mosby.

Miller, C. A. (2009). *Nursing for wellness in older adults* (5th ed.). Philadelphia: Wolters Kluwer Health.

Murray, S. S., McKinney, E. S., & Gorrie, T. M. (2006). *Foundations of maternal-newborn nursing* (4th ed.). Philadelphia: W. B. Saunders Company.

Niblett, V. (2006). *A nurse's guide to dosage calculation: Giving medications safely.* Philadelphia: Lippincott Williams & Wilkins.

Nies, M. A., & McEwen, M. (2007). *Community/Public health nursing: Promoting the health of populations* (4th ed.). St. Louis: Elsevier Saunders.

Pillitteri, A. (2007). *Maternal and child health nursing: Care of the childbearing and childrearing family* (5th ed.). Philadelphia: Lippincott Williams & Wilkins.

Potter, P. A., & Griffin Perry, A. (2007). *Basic nursing: Essentials for practice* (6th ed.). St. Louis: Mosby.

Potter, P. A., & Griffin Perry, A. (2009). *Fundamentals of nursing* (7th ed). St. Louis: Elsevier.

Potter, P. A., Griffin Perry, A., Ross-Kerr, J. C., & Wood, M. J. (2006). *Canadian fundamentals of nursing* (3rd ed.). St. Louis: Mosby.

Public Health Agency of Canada. (2005). *Norovirus fact sheet.* Retrieved December 8, 2008, from http://www.phac-aspc.gc.ca/id-mi/norovirus-eng.php

Quinn Youngkin, E., Sawin, K. J., Kissinger, J. F., & Israel, D. S. (2005). *Pharmacotherapeutics: A primary care guide.* Upper Saddle River, NJ: Pearson Prentice-Hall.

Rebraca Shives, L. (2005). *Basic concepts of psychiatric-mental health nursing* (6th ed.). Philadelphia: Lippincott Williams & Wilkins.

Registered Nurses' Association of Ontario. (2002). *Nursing best practice guidelines project.* Toronto: Author.

Ren Kneisl, C., & Trigoboff, E. (2009). *Contemporary psychiatric mental health nursing* (2nd ed.). Upper Saddle River, NJ: Prentice Hall.

Rice, R. (2006). *Home care nursing practice: Concepts and application* (4th ed.). St. Louis: Mosby.

Riley, J. B. (2008). *Communication in nursing* (6th ed.). St. Louis: Mosby.

Smeltzer, S. C., Bare, B., Hinkle, J. L., & Cheever, K. H. (2007). *Brunner and Suddarth's textbook of medical-surgical nursing* (11th ed.). Philadelphia: Lippincott Williams & Wilkins.

Smith Murray, S., & Slone McKinney, E. (2006). *Foundations of maternal-newborn nursing* (4th ed.). St. Louis: Elsevier Saunders.

Stanhope, M., & Lancaster, J. (2006). *Foundations of nursing in the community: Community-oriented practice* (2nd ed.). St. Louis: Mosby.

Stanhope, M., & Lancaster, J. (2008). *Community health nursing in Canada* (1st Canadian ed.). Toronto: Elsevier.

Stanhope, M., & Lancaster, J. (2008). *Public health nursing: Population centered health* (7th ed.). St. Louis: Mosby.

Stuart, G. W., & Laraia, M. T. (2005). *Principles and practice of psychiatric nursing* (8th ed.). St. Louis: Elsevier Mosby.

Stuart, G. W., & Laraia, M. T. (2009). *Principles and practice of psychiatric nursing* (9th ed.). St. Louis: Elsevier Mosby.

Taylor, C., Lillis, C., & LeMone, P. (2005). *Fundamentals of nursing: The art and science of nursing care* (5th ed.). Philadelphia: Lippincott Williams & Wilkins.

Taylor, C., Lillis, C., LeMone, P., & Lynn, P. (2008). *Fundamentals of nursing: The art and science of nursing care* (6th ed.). Philadelphia: Lippincott Williams & Wilkins.

Timby, B. K., & Smith, N. E. (2007). *Introductory medical-surgical nursing* (9th ed.). Philadelphia: Lippincott Williams & Wilkins.

Varcolis, E. M., Carson, V. B., & Shoemaker, N. C. (2006). *Foundations of psychiatric mental health nursing: A clinical approach* (5th ed.). St. Louis: Elsevier Saunders.

Wilkinson, J. M., & Van Leuven, K. (2007). *Fundamentals of nursing: Theory, concepts and applications*. Philadelphia: F. A. Davis Company.

Wong, D. L., Perry, S. E., Hockenberry, M. J., Lowdermilk, D. L., & Wilson, D. (2006). *Maternal child nursing care* (3rd ed.). St. Louis: Elsevier Mosby.

Yoder-Wise, P. S. (2007). *Leading and managing in nursing*. St. Louis: Elsevier.

Zator Estes, M. E. (2008). *Health assessment and physical examination* (4th ed.). Scarborough, ON: Thomson Nelson.